ROGER VAN I
in Boom, Belgiu
Gazet (Antwerp)

tice and wrote bittersweet, compassionate items about tormented figures. A gastrointestinal perforation in 1948 marked the beginning of a prolonged medical ordeal. In 1958, doctors prescribed Palfium, a highly addictive opioid. Van de Velde was caught forging prescriptions to feed his addiction and spent six of the last eight years of his life behind bars. In *Crackling Skulls* Van de Velde depicts his *compagnons de misère* in the psychiatric prison as men of flesh and blood, illustrating their insanity with respect and compassion. Van de Velde was released from the asylum in April 1970. Barely two months later, he died on an Antwerp café terrace of a Palfium overdose. He is buried among fellow noteworthy Belgian artists, musicians, and men and women of letters in the "artists' field of honor" at Antwerp's Schoonselhof Cemetery.

JONATHAN REEDER, a native of New York and longtime resident of Amsterdam, enjoys a dual career as a literary translator and performing musician. Alongside his work as a professional bassoonist he translates contemporary Dutch-language fiction by authors including Marjolijn van Heemstra, Martin Michael Driessen, A.F.T. van der Heijden, and Rodaan Al Galidi. He has a special fondness for Flemish literature, and has worked closely with Belgian writers Maarten Inghels, Rashif El Kaoui, Annelies Verbeke, Ish Ait Hamou, and Tom Lanoye.

ROGER VAN DE VELDE

CRACKLING SKULLS

TRANSLATED BY
JONATHAN REEDER

THIS IS A SNUGGLY BOOK

ISBN: 978-1-64525-113-2

This book was published with the support of
Flanders Literature (flanderliterature.be).

CONTENTS

Dedication / 7

Hercules Kneels / 11
Frozen Water / 15
Devalued Fetish / 20
A Decent Proposal / 27
Naked / 31
The Instructions of Prometheus / 35
Homily / 43
A Question Answered / 46
Jar of Pickled Herring / 52
Moshe Cheronim / 58
Monsieur Delcourt and the Worms / 66
Letter to the King / 77
Lesson in Philosophy / 83
The Rules of the Game / 88
White Was the Tomcat / 92
Margaritas Ante Porcos / 97
Artiste Peintre / 114

Livinus's Farewell / 120
Trumpet / 126
Unauthorized Items / 130

Translator's Note / 137

Life is a tale told by an idiot.
Macbeth

I had originally intended to dedicate these pages to those eccentric companions whom I spent all that time observing, by turns amused and alarmed, the way a child, in speechless wonder, watches the uninhibited cavorting and senseless chatter of baboons in the zoo. But what good is a printed dedication to them, with their crackling skulls? Most of them would make paper hats with it, and some, no doubt, would gladly gobble it up. Which might not be such a foolish thing after all. I just wanted to thank them for their unwitting collaboration.

The strangest and probably the best stories are not in this book, because there is a line where the inexplicable also becomes the inexpressible. Every time I set out to cross that line, I realized that words were simply inadequate.

Besides, it is time for me to stop stoking the embers of these morbid reminiscences, because I've been known to dream of them at night, and lie there screaming. To tell the truth, I'm as sick of this writing as I am of cold porridge. I have a life to live.

—Roger Van de Velde
Brussels, 1967

CRACKLING SKULLS

Frescos from an asylum

HERCULES KNEELS

It shouldn't have been possible, yet I saw it with my own eyes.

A hefty radiator unit raised above his head, Vukovic stormed, fuming, through the common room. He had ripped the bulky metal fixture from the wall with a few hard jerks and, armed with this menacing weapon, set out in pursuit of the yowling Sneyers, who desperately sought cover, of all places, under my chair.

Janos Vukovic was a hulk of a man with phenomenal strength. Elaborate tales of his herculean exploits made the rounds in the asylum, and they were only half-embellished. Legendary was his feat in the penitentiary, where he bashed three warders' heads together at once, knocking them out cold. Less wanton but equally impressive was when, on a wager, he hoisted the billiard table by one end to shoulder height and dragged it to the far end of the room. Tearing out the radiator added a new achievement to his track record of exceptional brawn.

Vukovic's nickname among the inmates was the Gypsy King. This romantic sobriquet was likewise only part fantasy. While no one knew for sure where or when he was born, the general consensus was that he belonged to a restless tribe of nomads that had fanned out from the Macedonian plateau to our own lowlands.

Like Hercules, Samson, and other delirious strongmen, Vukovic was kind at heart. He even seemed rather embarrassed by his enormous frame and the explosive energy bottled up in it. His sluggish movements gave the impression of safeguarding that energy against unwanted jolts, the way a truck driver maneuvers a ten-tonner packed with dynamite. He was a good-natured man, Janos Vukovic, but when he did blow his top, the dynamite blasted, leaving behind a heap of smoldering rubble. This happened occasionally in the asylum and also, alas, once on the outside.

So Vukovic menaced me with that leaden and leaking radiator raised above his head, while Sneyers cowered under my chair.

Everyone around took to their heels, and given the time and the opportunity, I would have done so myself. I was, however, busy rereading Flaubert, and while it is always an enjoyable read, *L'éducation sentimentale* was at that wretched moment of little use. I had never exchanged a harsh word with the Gypsy King, but from his bulging eyes it was clear I would not be spared if he could annihilate that rat Sneyers, and me along with him.

At that moment, Gerrit-with-the-lopped-off-fingers, in a fit of providential covetousness, mustered all his courage and launched a rear attack. It was the chance of a lifetime. For months, perhaps years, he had jealously eyed the Gypsy King's exquisite headdress: a vintage World War I infantryman's hat. A genuine "side cap" with a red tassel dangling merrily at the front. An ornament worthy of a king.

Gerrit slyly circled him, calculated his pounce like a cat, and in one swipe snatched the cap off the head of the unsuspecting Vukovic. The Gypsy King stiffened, nonplussed and defenseless, unsure who the bandit was.

Just then, reinforcements arrived. Six guards stormed the common room, poised for attack, armed with jangling handcuffs and thick billy clubs.

But it was no longer necessary. Janos Vukovic, the he-man Vukovic, slowly lowered the chunk of metal and sank to his knees, weeping, imploring the god of the gypsies to release him from this inhuman ordeal.

Then, contrary to all logic, something even more extraordinary happened. So extraordinary that it took my breath away as if I were witnessing a miracle. Gerrit-with-the-lopped-off-fingers, who under other circumstances might not shy away from murdering in cold blood to snag such a coveted prize, shuffled closer and silently handed over the side cap to the kneeling Gypsy King, who then truly broke down, now out of pure gratitude and joy. Vukovic donned his ornament and carried the severed radiator out back to the courtyard without giving Sneyers a second glance, the red tassel dangling merrily from his crimson head.

FROZEN WATER

Séraphin, a deaf-mute whose crime was a well-kept secret, slid a scrap of paper toward me across the tabletop. On it he had written, "Is it true that the human body is mostly made up of water?"

Séraphin often passed me notes like this. It was his sole means of communication, and at times our correspondence brought him intense joy. His inquiries were not limited to information or validation: often they were simple, self-evident observations or, on occasion, a personal opinion. For example: "Tibet is the roof of the world." Or, "It is a lie that Joshua made the sun stand still."

I had noticed that his queries or remarks, most of which referred to some item he had read in the newspaper or in the back issue of a magazine, were generally sensible and well thought out. Rarely did he pose an utterly absurd question devoid of rhyme or reason. And even when issuing a straightforward remark, he always insisted on a prompt reply in the form of a written confirmation, rebuttal, or explanation. We had an unspoken alliance that I found engaging on occasion, although sometimes it did put me in a tight spot. Like the time he asked, "What is the difference between the music of Beethoven and Bach?" The blind might learn to read with their fingers, but how, by what tangible means, can one possibly unfurl the subtle wonder of a fugue to a deaf-mute?

But the matter at hand was more straightforward, though it was unclear where all this was headed. On the back of the paper I wrote, "Indeed, the human body is composed mostly of water. I do not have the exact percentage at my fingertips, but I could look it up for you if you wish. Incidentally, it has been scientifically proven that all life originated in the sea."

His reaction was immediate. He impetuously ripped a page out of the yellowed issue of *Soir Illustré* he had been perusing, hastily scribbled something on it, and passed it to me.

It was a somewhat dated but nonetheless attractive color photo of Dorothy Lamour in a suggestive, flowered sarong. Underneath he had written in block letters: "This, too?" Smiling, I wrote back on the same page, "Yes, this, too. And it looks like goddamn delicious water. I would love to swim in it, wouldn't you?"

That "goddamn" was intentional, because I knew from experience that he took immense pleasure in graphic expletives. Even for someone who can neither speak nor hear, a robust curse, regardless of the medium, must also be a kind of release.

Nevertheless, he took no satisfaction whatsoever in my clarification. He sat somberly eyeing the photo for some time, slowly crumpled it into a wad, then went back to thumbing listlessly through the magazine. He composed no further missives.

I wondered what it was that vexed Séraphin about the chemical makeup of the human body. Fair enough, from an aesthetic point of view it is curious that even a bombshell like Dorothy Lamour was mostly made up of a substance as banal as water. But did this justify getting worked up over?

There must have been something else behind his ill humor. But since Séraphin avoided all contact, written or otherwise, for the rest of the evening, I gave it no more thought. It was by no means the first time he had suddenly, for no apparent reason, hermetically sealed himself away in the inaccessible bunker of his muffled mind. Once he sulked peevishly for days because I had honestly answered that as far as I knew, there was no reliable evidence whatsoever for, or any example of, life after death.

Two days after the inexplicable recusal of Dorothy Lamour, as I sat fumbling with my broken transistor radio, Séraphin suddenly slid me a new scrap of paper. Not without a certain pang of unease I read, "Does God exist?"

He had previously presented me with this very conundrum, with which humankind has been obsessed for the past six centuries, but I had always assiduously avoided divulging my views on the matter, for in its terrifying complexity I considered it far too volatile a subject.

This time, I sent back the rather reckless and simplistic reply, "All I know is what I see and understand. Where God is concerned, I see and understand nothing."

Again, he sat staring somberly at this hollow answer. Then came a new question:

"Presuming God does exist, why did he freeze the water in my mouth and ears?"

I looked pensively at the yellow and red wires inside the casing of my transistor radio and knew I had no answer for him. So I slowly stood up, with a chill in my spine. As I walked past, I briefly laid my hand on his shoulder.

DEVALUED FETISH

I hesitated for quite some time before deciding to have Evarist shave me. Not only because he was so unspeakably bad at it that surrendering oneself to his hands always carried a risk, but also (and chiefly) because I knew he harbored a profound grudge against me. I wouldn't put it past him to cheerfully slit my throat.

These things happen in an asylum. Some years earlier, a barber lost his temper with an obstreperous customer and gave him a nasty slice with his razor. The guard managed to intervene in the nick of time. When you think about it, it's highly irresponsible to trust a psychiatric patient with such a delicate business as shaving, but Evarist was considered to be completely harmless. Still, I had my doubts.

I could have petitioned the directorate for a different barber "for personal reasons." But then I would have been obliged to provide details about the nature and grounds of those personal reasons, and perhaps in my childish fear I had overestimated his animosity.

Besides, I could not resist the urge to test his temperament with a modest provocation. It was reckless of me to risk bleeding to death for the sake of an experiment, but I had always been drawn—often to my detriment—to danger and games of chance. And besides, I wanted to test my own courage, of which I am not always so certain.

Evarist's rancor was derived from a combination of sexual repression and, in all likelihood, injured pride.

One day he had presented me, beaming, with a crumpled photograph of a copious female nude. A professional *nu artistique* from one of the countless Parisian revues that have long been the haunt of teenagers and graybeards. And I have to confess she was indeed an appetizing wench, with buttocks and breasts ripe enough to sink one's teeth into, and I expressed my admiration for the aesthetic delight he so generously shared with me. But in a moment of carelessness I added, perhaps too flippantly, that such erotic images were a dime a dozen and could be found in pretty much any bookshop or sidewalk kiosk.

This remark was a psychological blunder, since by reducing his treasure to common merchandise, I had drastically devalued the fetish that Evarist so evidently held dear.

Exactly which cunning and clandestine maneuvers he had employed in order to obtain the photo in the first place, I never did find out. He had undoubtedly paid a premium for it, but that was his business. If he had just left it at that, he could have spent the rest of his days purring over the titillating image—a pleasure I would not have begrudged him in the slightest.

But Evarist in turn committed his own rash error. Like *le cocu magnifique*, he wanted to parade about with his conquest. As showy as a ruttish peacock, he flaunted his photo, showing off the voluptuous buttocks and breasts at every opportunity. His mania devolved into a sort of transcendental exhibitionism, if such a thing is possible, and after a few days he was being trailed by a string of drooling rubberneckers, who in their insatiable rapture begged to see it again and again, like the ecstatic disciples of the Virgin of Fatima.

The situation had the potential to develop into a dangerous group psychosis, and proprietors of an asylum fear collective sexual tensions like a burgeoning epidemic.

Anxious to protect Evarist from being caught with his magnetizing beloved, I tried, diplomatically, to convince him to use discretion in his colportage. Attracting the attention of the guards would invite catastrophe, I told him, for they would not hesitate to confiscate the source of his bliss. I was only trying to help, but by then the damage had already been done. That very afternoon, Evarist was summoned to the head office and thoroughly frisked; they hurled curses and abuse at him and seized his precious photo, which thenceforth most likely adorned the warden's bedroom. Evarist was lucky he was allowed to retain his barberly privileges.

Despite having no hard evidence whatsoever to justify such grave suspicions, Evarist was convinced that I had squealed on him, and let me know in no uncertain terms. When he returned from the office, humiliated and empty-handed, he marched straight at me, spat at my feet, and bellowed, "*Mouchard!*"

"Rat" was the asylum's harshest insult of all, commonly reserved for the lowest of the low. One could have murder, rape, or arson on one's conscience and still go about one's business undisturbed and with a minimum of scorn—but a *mouchard* was, in the eyes of those virtuous fellows, who spent most of their time in devious conclave conspiring to ensnare the others, an indisputable cretin, and undeserving of an iota of clemency.

It was my intention to simply ignore Evarist and his absurd suspicion, and to calmly let it fizzle. But meanwhile my beard kept growing, and I was not about to allow a *casus belli* brought about by the regrettable meanderings of a naked woman to turn me into a hirsute patriarch, nor let it encourage an unwarranted guilty conscience.

Evarist did not so much as bat an eye as I settled into the old armchair, a grubby towel draped around my neck. In the mirror I watched as he whetted the razor with quick, spiteful swipes on the leather strap, and how he frothed the soap with similar pique in a red shaving mug. I leaned my head back against the bar and closed my eyes, like a swimmer under water. If he entertained any ill intentions, I would certainly sense it. I could leap up in a flash, and the guard was close at hand. For ten minutes, Evarist attended to my face without mistreating even a single pore. Granted, he was a dreadful barber, with jerky strokes and sudden interruptions. But he was like that before, too, when I was still his friend. He acquitted himself to the best of his ability, and I could not claim that he purposely did me any harm. My disquiet took on another slant during those ten minutes, however, as I felt his hands glide under my nose and around my chin. Hands that tingled with the desire to explore a woman's body and to fondle its most intimate mysteries; hands with which he undoubtedly often masturbated. Realizing that those hands, probing gently like tentacles, yearned for slick vaginas filled me with more revulsion than the gradually ebbing fear of those same hands digging the razor deep into my throat. I clamped my lips firmly shut, mainly so as not to become infected with some nameless disease, but at the same time the blood rushed to my head; for could I, in all honesty, claim that my hands did not also yearn for buttocks and breasts and vaginas, even though I did not go around advertising it?

When I opened my eyes, Evarist was standing with his back to me, rinsing away the dirty lather. For the first time, I noticed his narrow, somewhat hunched back, and suddenly felt a strange sadness. Regret that he had been robbed of his photo, and remorse for having unjustly suspected him of ill will.

I thanked him quietly behind his bent back and laid three cigarettes on the zinc countertop beside the washbasin. This gesture was excessive: the customary fee for a shave was one cigarette, and in fact even that was not required, as he was paid for his work.

As I toweled my face dry, Evarist turned around and without a word broke the cigarettes in half, one by one, and threw them in the trash.

Those winsome girls, who in Paris and elsewhere trade their charms for a handful of cash, have no idea of the bitterness their buttocks and breasts can inspire in solitary men.

A DECENT PROPOSAL

Hilarion. To this day, I still wonder what possessed his parents to bequeath him such a wondrous lifelong epithet.

I knew of only one other Hilarion by name: an undoubtedly good-natured and devout pastor who, between morning mass and vespers, applied himself to composing cloying verses on a benificent God. Research also reveals a certain fourth-century abbot named Hilarion, who led a fellowship of ascetics in Palestine and whose name day is celebrated on the 21st of October. Just a bit of trivia I had read in *Snoeck's Almanac*.

Perhaps he was ashamed of his eccentric given name, because in the asylum he was known only as "Lamartine"—likewise a singular surname, for who can say "Lamartine" without it calling to mind the *Meditations poétiques* of his renowned namesake Alphonse?

It would probably have remained a secret if not for the letter. Ah, those letters! Once one of the guards had ascertained that I wrote with passable handwriting and nearly flawless grammar, the higher-ups officially anointed me public letter-writer in the service of my less literate comrades, who were forever wishing to inform their family of their excellent state of health—good news that was usually accompanied by an urgent request for care packages.

With the negligible start-up costs of a ream of paper and a bundle of ballpoint pens, I might, within a few short years, have earned a fortune as a public scrivener in Hong Kong, where I'm told the craft is still held in high esteem, and become a respectable man of independent means. I have written hundreds of letters of the most curious and rocambolesque nature, addressed to a dizzying array of dignitaries at home and abroad. In retrospect, I deeply regret not having faithfully kept copies of these missives, for they would comprise the most extravagant epistolary anthology imaginable. If even a commère like Mme. De Sévigné could get her cheap gossip printed, what publisher would not hurl himself upon correspondence addressed to emperors and kings, prelates and statesmen, generals, cycling champions, and Nobel prize winners?

That letter of Lamartine's, however, was a lost cause. He sidled over to my table with a sheet of lined writing paper, an envelope, and a postage stamp; by the esoteric sheen on his face, I presumed he had come on extremely delicate business.

My suspicions were confirmed when he presented me with a newspaper clipping, informing those with matrimonial aspirations that they could, under the strictest confidentiality, trust the matchmakers at "Happy Families" to secure them a tailor-made spouse with whom to embark on a rose-colored future.

I read the advertisement and sadly shook my head. "It's not allowed, Mr. Lamartine," I said.

This was true. Letters to strangers or suspicious associates, unfounded complaints, and appeals to charitable institutions were strictly prohibited by the censors. This matchmaking agency, despite adorning itself with the virtuous trappings of "Happy Families," clearly fell under the category of "suspicious organizations." Besides, Lamartine was fifty-seven years old, married, and the father of three children.

He handed me the oblation of a grossly overripe peach and smiled so sweetly that it was my moral duty to comply via a deceptive maneuver.

"Very well," I said. "What shall we write to the good people at 'Happy Families'?"

I knew full well that the letter would go straight into the warden's wastebasket, but if I didn't satisfy Lamartine, that mushy peach would undoubtedly end up in my face. His text was brief, respectable, and to the point: "The undersigned, Hilarion Lamartine, fifty-seven years of age, in good health and entitled to an invalid's pension, seeks matrimony with an attractive woman, likewise in good health, between thirty and forty years old, preferably well-situated."

It was a decent proposal, but it seemed to me at the very least a careless oversight not to mention his wife and three children.

I had him sign it. He did so with fervor, panting into my neck from the excitement. I affixed the postage stamp so that it could be easily peeled back off.

Before delivering the letter and the peach to the warden, I took another long look at Hilarion. There was no mistake: he had the unmistakable dog-like expression of a frustrated priest.

NAKED

"There is nothing quite so ugly as a naked man," wrote a French author, whose name has slipped my mind.

I was reminded of this unflattering observation when Scraps-and-Tatters walked into the dayroom stark naked. He had disrobed in the latrine, jammed his rags into the toilet, and marched, hideously naked but brimming with confidence, I would almost say dignified, into the room and installed himself in the middle of the old billiard table, like a dilapidated Buddha. I am open-minded in these matters, but it was truly an awful sight. When clothed, Scraps-and-Tatters' emaciated figure was already pitiful enough; naked, he was uglier than the most repulsive chimpanzee. I do not know whether physiognomists have ever considered drawing an analogy between the structure of a man's head and his genitals, but there must be a connection somewhere. In Scraps-and-Tatters' case the parallels were undeniable. His penis was as red and swollen as the nose on his face, and his pubic hair was as red as the curls on his neck. The Supreme Architect was having a decidedly off day when He botched up this specimen, both above and below.

I was not really surprised by Scraps-and-Tatters' exhibition. He had attempted it before. What surprised me this time, however, was his ability to maintain such serene and mystical detachment amid the unbridled hilarity that his spectacle provoked.

He sat cross-legged on the billiard table, immobile and arms folded, while the jeering mob pelted him with wads of paper, orange peels, slippers, ashtrays, tobacco tins, and anything else that lent itself to being thrown. Within a matter of minutes, the billiard table had been transformed into a garbage dump.

Under different circumstances, Scraps-and-Tatters would have retaliated against the bombardment and vigorously returned fire. Now, however, he seemed disturbingly immune to the senseless castigation. Occasionally he let out a bestial roar, like Quasimodo in his pillory, but even when he was struck on the left temple by an ashtray, he made no move to rub the painful spot. Normally I deplore grotesque parallels with heroic figures from the religious panopticon, but what can I say: he reminded me of the humiliated, bespat, and tormented Christ, passively beseeching his Almighty Father for mercy and forgiveness while drunken Roman soldiers pressed the crown of thorns upon his head. At least Christ, so say the Scriptures, was given a purple cloak with which to cover his broken body. The only purple on Scraps-and-Tatters was a jagged birthmark, rather like a squashed grape, on his left thigh.

As I sat musing on what mysterious motives might have driven Scraps-and-Tatters to this breathtaking display of masochism, the guard sauntered up. He knew there was no need to wait for reinforcements, as Scraps-and-Tatters was not aggressive. The guard knew exactly what needed to be done. He elbowed his way through the men thronging the billiard table and held out a bar of chocolate while softly whistling through his teeth, the way a pigeon-keeper might do from an attic window on a summer evening to lure his flock home.

This psychological maneuver worked like a dream. Scraps-and-Tatters clambered off the billiard table, grabbed the chocolate bar, and meekly allowed the warder to escort him out of the dayroom to the attendants' station, where a bundle of fresh clothes awaited him.

In his pathetic nakedness, Scraps-and-Tatters was as indescribably ugly from behind as from the front. And yet it was a touching, almost pastoral scene: this scrawny, sorry figure walking hand in hand with a trusted guide in white.

THE INSTRUCTIONS OF PROMETHEUS

Daniel smoked only three, at most four days a month, but then he smoked like a chimney from morning till night, let us say non-stop, the longest cigarettes I have ever laid eyes upon.

The first week of every month he would invariably place the same order at the canteen: seven pouches of "Louis Doize extra légères, sans filtre" and three packets of "Riz-la-Croix automatique gommé" rolling papers.

He would use the papers to roll triple-length cigarettes, which he meticulously stored in a flat, red-lacquered paintbrush box that was emblazoned with a Chinese dragon and which he carried with him at all times, like a cherished keepsake.

He smoked those improbably long cigarettes without the least ostentation. He sat calmly by himself in his usual, trusted spot at the table and exhaled, with quiet and earnest devotion, rhythmical blue puffs, like an imperturbable Arab silently sitting at his hookah as he meditates on Allah's unfathomable wisdom.

Nothing on Daniel's ascetic expression betrayed even an iota of emotion or satisfaction while he smoked. Only his eyes took on an oily luster, like the trance of an epileptic when a seizure is coming on.

I often observed him at a distance, and he appeared oblivious to any other presence in the overfull common room. Sometimes his measured, ritual gestures reminded one of the unhurried ceremony of a high priest, who in his brocade robe and with beringed fingers swings the censer and whose thoughts waft upwards, along with the smoke, to loftier regions.

After breakfast a guard would give Daniel a light for his first cigarette. He did not have to ask. The guard was an initiate to the ritual. He stood like a gangly choirboy in his white coat in the dining room doorway and would automatically take a box of matches from his pocket.

Then Daniel would commence his monthly smoking marathon lasting three, sometimes four days. He placed the paintbrush box holding his pre-rolled stockpile on the table before him like a miniature tabernacle and smoked his three-staged cigarettes without inhaling. With his yellowed fingertip he carefully flicked the ashes into a tin soapdish next to the paint-brush box and used the stub to light the next extra-long cigarette. I have never seen a more thorough demonstration of chain smoking. It was a perpetuum mobile that was interrupted only for meals and sleep. After each requisite interlude, the guard would silently offer him a new light and Daniel would silently continue his marathon.

Equally essential to the ritual was the presence of old Roupcinsky. He remained unwaveringly at Daniel's side for the duration of the smokefest. He sat next to him at the table, attentive and reverential, watched in rapt attention through the cloud of his cataracts and with a feverish blush on his cheeks while the long cigarettes slowly burned, and pounced like a hawk on its prey when a stub was deposited in the soapdish.

Roupcinsky was mad about cigarette stubs. He far preferred a handful of stubs to an entire pack of cigarettes ever since the warders forbade him to break whole cigarettes into pieces. The nicotine-drenched remains in the soapdish allowed Roupcinsky to chaw lavishly for a week. He, too, always carried a tin box with him, in which he kept the stubs. Queen Fabiola's image smiled from the lid, but Roupcinsky's banged-up tin was less attractive and more profane than Daniel's red-lacquered paintbrush box with the clawing Chinese dragon.

Daniel would habitually take an early afternoon stroll around the flowerbeds of the courtyard. He walked stiffly, because he lifted his rheumatic knees too high. To see him walking there with his long cigarette made one think of a quivering heron with a scrap of white driftwood in its beak. Roupcinsky stuck to him like a suckerfish and, leering and chawing, plucked the smoldering butts from amidst the dahlias and poppies as though they were glowworms.

Daniel's periodic smoke-mania was made possible by a providential sum of one hundred fifty francs, which was deposited by postal order in his name with calendric punctuality on the first of every month. The macenas was one Baroness Hélène Boxtyns de Lichtendaal. The stipend had been coming in for years, and no one in the asylum was able to trace the origins or nature of this mysterious relationship.

Daniel never spoke of the baroness. He signed the postal order in elegant, aristocratic handwriting without any further comment, as a payment he was rightfully due. Then he promptly placed his order with the canteen, puffed down his supply in three days, and did not touch a single cigarette for the rest of the month.

For Roupcinsky, the first week of the month was a treat. The brown juice constantly dribbled down his chin. For the next three weeks he paid Daniel no notice, but he impatiently counted the days until the first of the month, when he would again gloatingly station himself with his Fabiola tin at Daniel's side.

I wondered in vain why Daniel would go through his supply of cigarettes in a few days, and after that seem to suffer no craving whatsoever. It couldn't have been the nicotine high, for whenever I offered him a cigarette, he would always refuse it haughtily, almost with contempt. Maybe he would only smoke that one brand, I thought. In the third week of the month I bought a pouch of Louis Doize and a packet of Rix-la-Croix in the canteen. But when I, quasi-nonchalant, tried to slip it to him, he stared at me with such a terrifying expression that I hid away the unwelcome gift at once, as though it were some obscene object.

And yet I was not to be discouraged. My forever rekindled and insatiable curiosity was determined to find out why he would obsessively smoke such long cigarettes and then suddenly stop.

"Daniel," I asked him one day when he appeared well-disposed, "why do you smoke such long cigarettes?"

He looked at me with the eyes of a lizard. Every time he looked at me this way, it felt like a flock of startled pigeons flapped past above my head.

"I am following the instructions of Prometheus," he whispered.

"Who is Prometheus?" I asked.

"Prometheus is a spy," he replied, and paused for a moment to let his words sink in. "But you mustn't tell anyone," he added conspiratorially. "It's a secret between you and me."

I promised I would not tell anyone, but my further efforts to get to the bottom of the enigma went nowhere. Was he familiar with the story of Prometheus and his hollow reed? He must have heard or read somewhere that the myth had something to do with fire. But it remained a mystery what role the Baroness Hélène Boxtyns de Lichtendaal played in the affair. He did not utter a word about her, and for fear of driving him yet further into his shell, I dared not press him.

Did the baroness in one way or another suspect that the secret, thanks to the inquisitiveness of a brazen outsider, had been breached? Och, I'm just telling myself fairy tales.

But the fact of the matter is: on the first day of the following month no postal order arrived, nor the first of the month after that. The mysterious source of funds appeared to have suddenly run dry.

Daniel sank, day by day, into an ever more somber mood, and I feared that a crisis was imminent—the way the corners of his mouth trembled was the writing on the wall.

The crisis did not come, but at times he sat across from me at the table, his empty paintbrush box in front of him, glowering at me so black and hatefully that it gave me the shivers. It was just pure coincidence, naturally, but I felt ill at ease and a bit guilty for having stuck my nose into his secret bond with Prometheus.

After six weeks, I couldn't stand it any longer. I bought three pouches of Louis Doize and two packets of Riz-la-Croix, rolled a dozen extra-long cigarettes, and deposited them without a word on the table next to the paintbrush box.

And then came Daniel's crisis. He let out an earsplitting shriek, ran through the common room on his spindly legs, disappeared into the cupboard behind the kitchen, and drank a quarter of a bottle of Eau de Javel before the guard could intervene.

He was rushed to the hospital, his insides on fire and a greenish froth on his lips.

Fortunately, the damage was minimal. Leonard, who lay in the same hospital with prostate troubles, wrote just a week later that Daniel had recovered quickly and gorged himself on oranges, which was surely a good sign.

Shortly thereafter, one of the guards informed me that Daniel, thanks to intervention by his family, would be transferred to another asylum. Was it on the instruction of Baroness Boxtyns de Lichtendaal? I never found out.

After that I saved my cigarette stubs in a cardboard box for Roupcinsky.

HOMILY

Félicien had died, and after dinner the warder called upon us to spare a thought for the deceased in our prayers. He asked it very quietly, the warder, as though making some kind of indecent proposal.

Very well. *Requiem aeternam dona eis, Domine*. All the best, Félicien, may your soul rest in peace, even though it is tainted by a dark blot, which will be the subject of some serious deliberation on Judgement Day. But who are we to judge? So: all the best.

But what about the body surrounding the soul in question? Five minutes before he died, Félicien voided his bowels for the very last time. He was literally in deep shit when he met his maker. And frankly, he probably didn't even mind.

God of the warder, whoever and wherever you may be, if you are looking down on these words, please forgive this undignified imagery. But since people say you are the eternal truth, then surely it's fitting that the truth accompany the gravity and the solemnity of a man's ultimate moment.

A small part of your eternal truth is that Félicien died in his own shit, as most people who die in a lamentable *laisse-aller* tend to do. And the truth is that during his seven years in the asylum, he lay in his own excrement more often than not. Because, lame in both legs, he was simply unable to get himself out of bed. And because the attendants were too lazy, or too distracted, or too busy with other patients to slide the bedpan under his ass in time.

And the truth is that on occasion, he lay stinking for hours in his own vomit, again because those crippled legs kept him anchored to the bed like lead weights. Another truth is that he died of pneumonia at the age of forty-two, because the draft from the latrines blew straight at his bed, and because his only form of preventative medicine was three spoonfuls daily of "Potion des Carmelites" cough syrup.

And, God of the warder, the truth is also... But what difference does all this make to Félicien's immortal soul?

Let us hope that his soul fares better than his body did, now that there's nothing left of it, even though for the seven years prior to his death it wasn't worth a tinker's damn either.

And vis-à-vis that dark blot: perhaps it would be better if his soul weren't so immortal after all, and it discreetly perished along with his body.

If, by chance, the eternal truth also means that with death, everything ceases to exist—joy and suffering, hope and pain, yearning and misery, and especially that bothersome excrement—then Félicien has finally found paradise after all.

A QUESTION ANSWERED

Why is it that since serving time, I seem to have so much to do with Greeks? I don't speak an iota of modern Greek and have, alas, forgotten most of the ancient kind. I have never visited Greece and do not even have a Grecian nose. What bizarre affinity attracts me to them, or them to me?

There was Dimitrios Christos Papathanassiou, the one with the mustache and the marijuana, whose gibberish helped him wriggle his way out of detention. Then there was Andreas Nikolakis, who sat trembling with bloodied hands in Leuven Central Station at the thought of all those bleak penitentiary years ahead of him. And now there was Suzapoulos (no idea if I have spelled his name correctly), who, only the fickle gods of Greece know how and why, lumbered into the asylum.

He was sitting across from me in the dentist's waiting room, and the way he rolled a cigarette at once told me he was a foreigner. He kneaded the tobacco into a ball in the palm of his hand, placed it in his mouth to moisten it, and rolled the cigarette with the thumb and index finger of one hand, just like I once saw Gary Cooper do in an old western.

But more striking than his rolling technique was his physique. He was so tall and lean that it pushed the limits of physical possibility. His legs were an anatomical joke. His narrow blue cotton trousers ended at his calves, and no matter how he tried, he was unable to contort his legs into a comfortable position. I put him at well over six feet as he uncrumpled himself and made his way towards me.

"Would you be so kind as to give me a light?" he asked in English, from his imposing altitude.

He had a virile, mellifluous voice with a Byzantine twang that did not at all resemble Gary Cooper's, and which I was unable to place at first. In the flicker of my match, his eyes glistened like those of an innocent angel on a faded icon. With those legs and that voice and those eyes, the hippies of San Francisco would have welcomed him with open arms. But then, San Francisco was so very far away.

He folded himself back onto his seat and stared at me so intently that it gave me the jitters. I felt the need to break the silence.

"How are things in the States?" I inquired ambiguously.

"I have never been to the States," he replied. "I am Greek." He blew smoke out of his nostrils the way a bull in a comic book does, and there was a vague sadness in his tone. Or was it the shame of coming from such a hopelessly broken country?

I could not just let him sit there with that sadness and shame. So I rephrased my question to "How are things in Greece?" as a sort of gesture of sympathy.

He shrugged his sagging shoulders. "Greece is one big prison," he replied with such resolve and scorn that there was no arguing with it. But it was odd to hear this rigorous judgment from the mouth of someone who, dishearteningly far from home, found himself in a Belgian jail.

"Yes, so they say," I answered, hoping to put this discussion to rest. Under the circumstances, international politics seemed a rather delicate topic. Based on his remark I presumed he was on the "right" side, but this did not mean one could safely badmouth the dictator Papadopoulos and his colonels. He was clearly against a regime that threw dissenters into dungeons by the truckload, but that didn't rule out that he was still, despite everything, loyal to the crumbling monarchy. I briefly considered raising the issue of Cyprus and Turkey as a change of tack, but wisely decided against poking that particular hornet's nest.

Our diplomatic silence did not last long.

"How long am I going to stay in jail?" he asked point-blank.

It was a straightforward question that demanded a straightforward answer. But what could I say? I knew nothing of his past, and equally little of his future. "This is not a jail, it's a hospital," I corrected him in a schoolteacherly manner. This was an outright lie—no one was more aware of the bitter truth than I—but I hoped that my grotesque euphemism would nonetheless go some way to alleviating his inauspicious prospects.

"How long?" he persisted. He restlessly shuffled his stilty legs, and I grew uneasy beneath his intense gaze.

"Not long," I answered evasively, eyeing his endless legs with trepidation. Where, I wondered, would one find a bed in which to stretch those things?

“I’m not a criminal,” he stressed. “I’m broke, that’s all. No money, no family, no nothing. Surely that’s not a crime?”

“Not at all,” I ventured, mindful that men without money, family, or anything to hang onto tend to resort to strange behavior. And one only need glance though Hellenistic mythology to ascertain that the heirs of Pyrrha have had more than their fair share of tragedies.

“If it’s not a crime in this country to have nothing and nobody, then I don’t belong in wretched place like this,” he said with unshakable certainty. “How long are they going to keep me here?”

The question that was so vexing him now truly called for an answer.

“A few days, maybe a week,” I said blithely and against my better judgement.

The smile of an excited child unfurled upon his angelic face. “Are you sure it will only be a matter of some days?” he asked.

“Absolutely,” I shamelessly lied. I knew it would be months or perhaps years, but I could not bring myself to just throw this at him.

Just then, the waiting room guard called out: “Susapoulos.” Or something to that effect. It sounded melodious, like “Zoozaypalooss.”

He stood up, rose to his appreciable height, and came over and shook my hand. "Thank you so much, sir," he said. "I sincerely hope they won't keep you for long, either." And before he entered the dentist's office, he turned towards me once again with that disarming, childlike smile of a Greek Gary Cooper.

I smiled back reassuringly and felt so indescribably miserable that I could have broken down sobbing then and there. But my tears had dried up long ago.

JAR OF PICKLED HERRING

Although I knew better than to underestimate the Marquis De la Motte and was always on the qui-vive in my dealings with him, he still managed to find ways to catch me off guard.

The Marquis owed me the sum of thirteen million francs for services rendered over the previous six months. And then, when I least expected it and for no apparent reason, he heartily and firmly placed a jar of pickled herring in my hand. Evidently, I was supposed to consider this unexpected gift the quittance of his debt and proof of his solvency.

I accepted his sour "fruits of the sea" with the obligatory words of gratitude but was deeply suspicious of the gesture. It was not the Marquis De la Motte's style to repay his debts in kind. On the contrary, his shameless scrounging and schnorring knew no bounds. Everyone knew from experience how ill-advised it was to leave belongings unattended when he was around.

Besides, the Marquis was not allowed to be in possession of dangerous objects like glass jars, no matter how innocent the contents. Two years earlier, in a fit of dark desperation, he had attempted to slit his wrists with the sharp edge of a sardine tin, and when that failed, he swallowed the shards of a crushed drinking glass. It had cost him a nasty abdominal hemorrhage, and later, on the operating table, a piece of his stomach. So in light of the potential for self-mutilation, a glass jar was like an unpinned grenade.

I assumed that some gullible sucker had "sold" him the jar of herring for an astronomical amount, for the Marquis De la Motte threw around his fictitious millions with a nonchalance that would put Onassis to shame. He would saunter ostentatiously from table to table, a notebook tucked under his arm, indescriminately writing out IOUs for dizzying amounts. For a friendly word, a smile, a cigarette, or a cup of coffee, he would at once issue a promissory note along the lines of: "The undersigned owes the holder the sum of three hundred thousand francs." And underneath, his signature: *Marquis Jacques De la Motte.* Never mind that he didn't have a marquisial pot to piss in; in just a few years he must have handed out many billions of imaginary francs. Though he himself probably obtained the most pleasure from all this munificence, it was to his credit that his wild charade also imparted some joy to his fellow inmates.

The Marquis rewarded my favors extra-lavishly, thanks to my initial and rather reckless fertilization of his unbridled imagination with some bizarre ideas of my own. He was a born conspirator, fixated on undermining authority, and was forever plotting spectacular escapes, the violent abolition of prisons and asylums, and the merciless annihilation of the clergy (he was, for reasons unknown to me, a staunch atheist). This, too, was in keeping with his rabid anarchism. Rather than the pompous title "Marquis De la Motte," which he had undoubtedly found somewhere in a book on the French Revolution, he ought instead to have chosen the epithet "Ravachol." Although, when signing checks worth millions of francs, an aristocratic title is certainly more impressive than a terrorist one.

My highest ever fee from the Marquis was to the tune of four million francs for an ingenious, albeit quite absurd, plan for an escape by levitation. For years he had been obsessed with the idea of breaching the high wall, which was topped with barbed wire and broken glass and represented the tangible barrier to equally tangible millions. Having dismissed the classic methods of digging a tunnel or scaling the wall using a makeshift bedsheet rope as amateurish and unworkable, as well as discounting blasting his way out with nitroglycerin due to lack of raw materials, he toyed with the notion of vaulting his way to freedom, based on the conviction that a well-trained athlete should be able to reach a height of five meters. Four meters was already enough to nip over the wall.

I managed, not without difficulty, to talk him out of this plan, for he was prepared to experiment with poles and pikes, and was liable to break his neck in the process. As compensation I casually mentioned the appealing and innocuous method employed by various mystics and inspired prestidigitators of the past, who would raise themselves off the ground aided solely by willpower and concentration. The spiritual archives claimed that it was all a matter of blind faith, although Newton later provided sound scientific evidence to the contrary.

Despite his zealous skepticism of anything even hinting at religious propaganda, the

Marquis enthusiastically embraced the notion of miraculous levitation. He was prepared to write me a check for four million francs on the spot, provided I observe absolute confidentiality. I told him three million would suffice, but he insisted on four. A million francs per levitated meter was, he felt, fair recompense.

I never again enjoyed such a windfall. He did once write out an IOU worth two million for a proposal to abolish the clergy via the universal and controlled introduction of immaculate conception as *condicio sine qua non* for mothers of all future priests, monks, and nuns. But the failure of his dogged attempts at levitation, despite all his concentration and willpower, must have left him deeply disillusioned. So much so, in fact, that he moved on to a more utilitarian approach, for one day he came to me for advice in expediently bumping off the director of the asylum. I missed my big chance, because he was prepared to offer me a record-breaking ten million francs for any workable idea. Shocked and perturbed by his plan, however, I declined any further collaboration. Not that I thought the director was a particularly sympathetic figure, but I felt it was better for him to meet a more peaceable end.

Did the Marquis De la Motte resent my refusal, after having showered me with favors for so long? I thought so at first, because for the next three weeks he wouldn't give me the time of day. I even feared he would rescind his previous IOUs, which would have spelled a definitive rupture between us.

Until, entirely unexpectedly and with no apparent desire for reciprocity, he came trotting up to me with that jar of pickled herring, like a child bearing a posy of flowers.

I was both relieved to see him voluntarily surrender this dangerous instrument and touched that the Marquis De la Motte seemed capable of a concrete gesture of generosity after all. In a way, it validated all his worthless millions.

And still, I did not trust it.

Of course, my suspicions were justified. When I opened the jar that evening to salute the s health with some herring on a slice of bread, the rotten fish spread its stench through the dining hall like a putrid gust of the Bubonic plague.

MOSHE CHERONIM

After not even five minutes in the dayroom, he was already the center of attention, thanks to his curious appearance and eccentric conduct.

It was his attire that drew the most notice. Nearly all of us wore old Canadian World War II uniforms, dyed a deep sea blue. Or occasionally, by explicit doctor's orders, striped pajamas. Some inmates permitted themselves vestmental frivolities such as vintage hats, paper decorations, colorful scarves, and flapping shirttails, but further clownery was not tolerated.

The diminutive fellow came into the dayroom wearing the standard-issue blue uniform, but draped over his shoulders was a brownish saddlecloth with broad white stripes. On the back of his head was a minuscule skullcap, and framing his slender neck was a jet-black beard, parted in the middle. This combination of decorative saddlecloth and Assyrian beard elicited much hilarity, because facial hair was normally forbidden, for reasons of personal hygiene.

As a circle of curious and chortling onlookers formed around him, the little man positioned himself facing the whitewashed wall alongside the warden's station and, ignoring the inquisitive hubbub, began to rock back and forth, mumbling texts from a thick, black, leather-bound book, like a tzaddik in prayer. His voice had a guttural timbre and his body rocked rhythmically back and forth, as in a trance.

The throng of spectators grew. When Gerrit-with-the-lopped-off-fingers, who was always on the lookout for potential booty, made moves to snatch the saddlecloth, and an imminent fracas was in the air, the guard came strutting over and gruffly shouted, "About your business!"

The gawkers grudgingly circulated, and the little Jew, unperturbed, continued bobbing and chanting at his whitewashed station, which for him was undoubtedly a symbolic segment of the Wailing Wall.

The sheepish, moonfaced guard spent a few indecisive moments observing the wondrous performance. Then he sidled up to me.

"You couldn't persuade the rabbi to turn over his saddlecloth, could you?" he asked. "Regulations, y'see. I doubt he'll do so willingly, and the fellow doesn't speak a word of French or Dutch."

The guard had seen me reading English books before. Apparently, he was of the opinion that since Balfour, all Israelites made a point of learning the language of their protectors, and he saw me as a potential interpreter.

I thoroughly loathed the task before I even started it. "Let's say he does speak English," I grumbled, "and say he's not inclined to cooperate. Do the regulations say I have to wrestle the saddlecloth from him?"

The guard smirked. "Not necessarily," he said. "It might go peacefully. He doesn't seem like the fighting type."

"What's your rabbi's name, then?" I inquired. If a conversation was unavoidable, it could at least be conducted on polite terms.

The guard consulted his notebook and, with difficulty and in an abominable accent, squeezed out a name. His attempt sounded something like "Moshe Cheronim."

I sighed, got up, and ambled over to the man, briefly noting that my good nature had once again been taken advantage of. I addressed him with a viscid and, for the occasion, as guttural a tone as possible. "Excuse me, Mister Cheronim?"

The little Jew mumbled for another ten seconds, and then looked at me with the brown eyes of a gazelle.

"I suppose you speak English," I said, glad for such a speedy and, for the moment, harmonious response.

He continued to look at me intensely but did not reply.

With my most well-meaning smile, I gestured to a nearby table, for I felt the conversation would go more smoothly seated than standing. While his swaying had ceased, there was still a slight tremor in his stance, as though the cadence might resume at any moment. Behind us, the guard had taken a few discreet steps back, but he stayed close enough in order to seize the saddlecloth at the first available opportunity.

The little Jew shut his prayerbook, made a devout gesture over it, and obligingly sat down with me at the table.

"Glad to make your acquaintance," I said ceremoniously. "My name is Roger. Is there anything I can do for you?"

He still did not answer, but from a deep pocket he produced a pack of cigarettes and proffered it to me with a hairy, well-groomed hand.

Although I never smoke filter cigarettes, my sense of good manners forbade me from turning down his offer. You never know what the Talmud says about a rebuffed gift.

I took a cigarette and thanked him, as one does.

Still holding the pack in my face, he raised three fingers on his other hand.

I looked puzzled, but he nodded encouragingly for me to take two more. Perhaps he was under the mistaken impression that I had sought out his company in order to mooch cigarettes from him.

Disinclined to refuse this unasked-for gift, I gingerly laid the additional cigarettes on the left side of the table, well out of reach of Gerrit, who was still hovering to one side, eyeing the loot. I gave Moshe Cheronim a light and resumed my efforts at getting a conversation going.

"Excellent cigarettes," I said. "I like them very much." It sounded embarrassingly banal, and was moreover a barefaced lie, for filter cigarettes always taste to me like perfumed hay.

Still no reply. I had to change tack. "Sprechen Sie Deutsch?" I asked. Since Kaltenbrunner, I figured, all Jews probably spoke a smattering of German.

No response. I sat there shamelessly smoking his cigarettes and trying in vain to tell him what a fine fellow he was, while searching for a way to diddle him out of his saddlecloth, to which he was undoubtedly dearly attached.

I was suddenly overcome with a sense of self-loathing, and besides, my vocabulary had run dry. I considered trying Latin, but you could hardly expect a Jew who spoke neither English nor German to be conversant in the lingo of the Vatican.

I cautiously pointed to his shawl and tried, with an approving smile, to indicate that I thought it a fine piece of textile. "Hevel havolim, kuloy hevel," he said. These words, his first, were as unfathomable to me as a Kabbalistic anagram from a Torah scroll. Was it an expression of friendship? Was it a curse? Was he commenting on the weather? I had no idea, and by now I did not care.

I made a show of lighting the other two cigarettes as though they were gifts of gold and myrrh, bowed courteously *comme il faut*, and left him behind in all his inscrutability. It's possible that my hasty departure offended him, but I could hardly be expected to make off with his saddlecloth like some wily Arab. It was already bad enough that I had robbed him, against my will, of three unsmokeable filter cigarettes.

With my hands in my pockets, I walked off and, in passing, grumbled to the guard, "Hevel havolim, kuloy hevel, and leave me out of your lousy shenanigans."

When I went to the latrine half an hour later, the little Jewish man was elaborately making water, with a line of four men waiting behind him. With only three toilets serving a ward of a hundred and ten, there was always a line. Using the toilets had also become a public operation, ever since Marynissen hanged himself on the cistern six months ago and they tore down the doors.

Moshe Cheronim's business lasted a good ten minutes. He peed copiously, with the gushing discharge of a horse, and all the while he stood swaying to and fro, as before at the wall. How such an enormous amount of urine could be squeezed into the bladder of such a diminutive man was a mystery to me.

Things grew heated behind him, and there was enthusiastic applause when Lionel exclaimed in his childish voice, "Go piss in Jerusalem, ya rotten Yid!"

When Moshe Cheronim, or whatever his name was, finally turned around, the slightest of smiles appeared above his beard. It was the most pathetic and disdainful smile I have ever seen, and it made my blood run cold.

Then off he went, still draped in his saddlecloth, back to his post at the whitewashed wall, and quietly resumed his recitations without paying the slightest heed to the bevy of rubberneckers that again clustered around him. This time he ignored me, too. He must have felt as isolated and inviolable as Yahweh in paradise.

MONSIEUR DELCOURT AND THE WORMS

It was during the midday meal of mashed potatoes, red cabbage, and a frankfurter sausage that Bernard Delcourt first saw the worms.

I was seated diagonally across from him, and as I was put off by the food, I sat listlessly taking in the sight of the other men eating. Those grotesque mugs, and the sucking and slurping sounds they produced, was anything but appetizing.

Bernard Delcourt was an anemic man in his fifties, with an absurd and completely useless ring of reddish hair encircling his bald scalp and a metal lorgnette balanced on his can-opener of a nose. Behind his glasses (which can only have dated from the previous century, and to which he was very attached, not only because of his myopia), a pair of restless eyes flickered like steel pellets in his sickly face. He was the typecast office clerk in an amateur theater company.

Bernard Delcourt was not what you would call friendly. He was too skittish to seek the company of others, and therefore left everyone alone. This was his only merit. Otherwise, in his scarce words and gestures he was extremely well-mannered, and this civility earned him certain privileges. The guards addressed him, entirely without sarcasm, as "Monsieur Delcourt," and as a rare indulgence, he was the only inmate allowed to wear his own calfskin shoes.

He was also one of the few inmates whom the doctor afforded the liberty of choosing his own books from the library. Curiously, despite his precious mannerisms, he had a clear preference for the French realists and naturalists. He read and reread works by Sue, Flaubert, De Maupassant, Zola, and Huysmans, diligently taking notes in a thick school notebook which he kept under lock and key. He had read *Madame Bovary* so often that he must have known large tracts of it by heart. But what, pray tell, could Madame Bovary have to do with the worms?

That the incident occurred while eating mashed potatoes, red cabbage and a frankfurter sausage is a detail I recall vividly, because

Monsieur Delcourt, in a show of utter disgust, spat a glob of mushy, half-chewed food back onto his plate. At first, I took it to be blood, but what dribbled over the sausage turned out to be red cabbage mashed up with saliva.

I gagged and my stomach lurched, while my tablemates simply glanced up for a moment in surprise, and then returned to their meals with gusto. That the typically so proper Monsieur Delcourt had abandoned his decorum both shocked and annoyed me.

The guard approached the table, slowly but resolutely, and arched his eyebrows as a sign of disapproval.

"Anything the matter, Monsieur Delcourt?" he asked calmly and a tad condescendingly, the way an unflappable schoolmaster addresses a misbehaving pupil.

Delcourt did not answer. He sat paralyzed, staring at his plate and at the slimy spittle as though hypnotized by it.

"Are you unwell?" the guard asked, his voice raised slightly but with no angry undertone.

Delcourt's beady eyes remained glued to his plate. He raised a bony finger and pointed to the pink mush without a word passing over his bloodless lips. Next to him, Lamartine sat giggling like a ticklish schoolgirl. He found the situation highly amusing.

The guard snapped his fingers and the kitchen boy trudged out to collect the mess. He held the plate at arm's length as though it were loaded with excrement, his head twisted to one side and his nose ostentatiously in the air. The performance was so entertaining that the dining room grew unruly. The guard clapped loudly a few times, indicating that mealtime was over, and the men rushed to the exit to debate on what terrible punishment awaited Bernard Delcourt.

Delcourt stayed put, stock-still and with a blank gaze behind the shimmering lenses of his lorgnette.

The guard positioned himself in front of him, arms crossed and feet planted wide, and patiently repeated his earlier question: "What is the matter, Monsieur Delcourt?"

Without budging, Delcourt whispered with enigmatic contempt, "The filthy creatures."

"What creatures?" the guard sighed. He had already dealt with so many creatures in such obscure varieties, the ceaseless zoological phenomena were truly beginning to bore him.

"Worms," replied Delcourt. There was a cold quiver in his voice. "Filthy, slimy worms."

Of course, worms, the guard thought to himself. It nearly always starts with worms, but what menacing monsters would be next? One never knew. The guard was starting to build up quite some experience in psychiatry.

"What kind of worms?" he inquired, with endless patience. "Red, white, yellow, black?"

"Orange," answered Delcourt. "Long, fat, orange worms."

A new color for our collection, thought the guard. Orange doesn't strike me as an aggressive color. Pending further study, orange worms are definitely preferable to the black ones, because the darker they are, the more trouble they seem to cause.

He patted Delcourt reassuringly on the shoulder. "We've got a remedy for that," he said. "I'll give you a sip of something that will wipe out those rotten worms, and you'll be feeling better within the hour."

That evening the guard, quite pleased with himself, wrote in the patient logbook: "Monsieur Delcourt prétend voir des vers de couleur orange. Je lui ai administré dix gouttes de RL-793, conformément aux instructions du médecin-psychiatrie, Dr. Poulard. Une demi-heure avant le coucher le malade me parait décontracté."[1]

---

1 "Monsieur Delcourt claims to be seeing orange-colored worms. I administered ten drops of RL-793, in accordance with the instructions of Dr. Poulard, psychiatrist. Half an hour before retiring to bed, the

Delcourt had a peaceful night. The next morning, he was given another ten drops of RL-793 in a glass of water, which he accepted without argument. In fact, he gulped it down. He did, however, obstinately refuse to enter the dining room. The guard tried using gentle pressure but gave up after three failed attempts. Here we go again, he thought dispiritedly, another hunger strike. But at that same moment he had to turn his attention to the Count Van Orléans, who was busy chastising the cripple Semmelinck with a wooden spoon. Despite his chlorpromazine, the count was becoming more difficult by the day.

Dr. Poulard, too, appeared to attach some significance to the orange color of the worms, for after perusing the report, he said, to the guard's delight, "Remarkable."

Dr. Poulard was an old-school psychiatrist, the type that went to great lengths get to the bottom of things. In the present case, it was clear that his diagnosis should focus on a possible amalgam of animal hallucinations and sensitized color associations, bringing on a trauma of some sort. Intuitively, the guard knew this already, but he was at a loss for how to proceed. And frankly, Dr. Poulard was, too.

---

patient appeared to have relaxed."

"Let's see," the doctor said. "Was the patient threatened in any way recently with an object of that particular color? Everyone knows, of course, that orange is a derivative of the primary colors yellow and red. Delcourt's trauma could have been brought about by a combination of hostility and anger. What hateful object could have triggered Monsieur Delcourt's anger?"

The guard had no ready answer. And to be honest, he did not see what this color combination had to do with the worms. If man's subconscious were truly worm-eaten by hostility and anger, then worms would certainly be the world's undoing. Since he hesitated to share these musings with Dr. Poulard, the guard simply shrugged his shoulders.

"As far as I know, there are no distinctly orange-colored objects around," he ventured. Just to be sure, he checked the lampshades on the hanging fixture, but these were distinctly red. In the evening, the common room always resembled a brothel.

"Living beings are also objects," the psychiatrist pointed out. "Is there perhaps someone, a fellow patient or a member of staff, with a tinted skin color tending toward orange? Certain Mongolian races, for instance, exhibit a pronounced orange pigment. Just a thought."

Stoffels, thought the guard. Stoffels, whose bad liver made him look like a down-at-the-heel Chinese mandarin. He dismissed this theory at once, however, as Stoffels had been in the infirmary for the past two months, and prior to that had little contact met Delcourt.

"It could, of course, be purely psychological," the doctor continued. He had neither the time nor the appetite for scouring the area for every orange-colored object. "What is Monsieur Delcourt reading these days?"

The guard fetched the borrowing card from the library. The names were neatly lined up, a bit outmoded yet still presentable with their impassioned opuses: Flaubert, Sue, De Maupassant, Zola.

"Remarkable," the psychiatrist said a second time.

The guard nodded in agreement, although he couldn't for the life of him see what was so remarkable about the yellowed pages of a bunch of nineteenth-century fantasists.

"The patient often takes notes while reading," he said. If Flaubert was so remarkable, then maybe Delcourt's scribblings were also worth reading.

"You might have told me that earlier," the doctor said, with a hint of reproach. "I should like to peruse those notations, if I may."

The guard got up and went into the common room, where Delcourt was sitting forlornly in a corner, fretting about the worms.

"May I borrow the key to your locker, Monsieur Delcourt?" he asked. He had his own copy of the key in his pocket, but regulations dictated that personal belongings were not to be touched without the owner's permission. Except in case of emergency. And this was, for the time being, not an emergency.

Delcourt silently handed over the key. He mechanically did everything that was asked of him, except eating worm-infested food.

Dr. Poulard leafed inquisitively through the notebook, but its contents proved disappointing. Mainly sentimental descriptions of idyllic or dramatic events at sunset or by moonlight. Not a word about vermin.

"Those so-called realists and naturalists—no more than romantic dreamers, really," the doctor said, a bit blasé. He suppressed a burp and wondered where on earth he was going to track down that anger and hostility.

"Let's have a word with Delcourt," he said. "Perhaps he can tell us something."

There was, however, nothing Delcourt could tell them. He responded to neither relevant questions nor irrelevant ones; he only stared obsessively through his lorgnette at a pinkish pimple on the psychiatrist's cheek.

Dr. Poulard in turn looked questioningly at the guard, as though he might offer some suggestion, and eventually shrugged his shoulders.

"Let's give it a few more days," he said. "Perhaps it will sort itself out. After all, orange is a secondary color and we've seen these kinds of worms before. They come and go. Continue administering RL-793, and try to coax him into eating something. Preferably solid food: dry biscuits, chocolate, and the like. But do not force him. There's no harm in fasting for a few days. If there's no progress in three days' time, we'll put him on intravenous feeding."

He glanced through the remaining reports, prescribed an increased dose of chlorpromazine for the Count Van Orléans, and telephoned his wife to say he was on his way home for lunch.

No harm indeed in a few days' fast, the guard thought, and he gave Delcourt, who was gratifyingly calm for the rest of the day, no further notice.

But at bedtime his restlessness returned. He lay in bed, wretched and whining like a frightened dog, baying at the orange light of the moon.

When Gaston – the old night warden who was edging toward senility but was still firm on his feet – returned from his rounds, he wrote in the patient logbook with arthritic fingers: "Monsieur Bernard Delcourt souffre d'un rhume. Il tousse lamentablement. Je lui ai administré une cuillère de sirop pectoral, dose forte, conformément aux instructions du médecin-interniste Dr. Hoffman dan un cas pareil. Une demi-heure plus tard le malade s'est endormi."[1]

Half an hour after the "sirop pectoral, dose forte," Monsieur Delcourt did indeed fall asleep, a deep sleep from which he would never awaken. His body, it seemed, was ready for the worms.

---

1 "Monsieur Bernard Delcourt is suffering from a cold. He has a miserable cough. I administered a spoonful of cough syrup, a strong dosage, compliant with the instructions of Dr. Hoffmann in such cases. The patient fell asleep 30 minutes later."

LETTER TO THE KING

Jerome Corthals, who could neither read nor write, dictated the following letter to the king, which I faithfully notated and duly sent. To my knowledge, there was no reply.

Sire,

As a frontline soldier during the Great War, fourteen months in the trenches at the Yser, eight months in a field hospital with one leg shot off above the knee, and a chest full of medals, I, Corthals, Jerome Cornelius Alfonsina, sixty-six years old, take the humble liberty of addressing Your Majesty to inform you that this situation is untenable.

Wrongly locked up for the past nine years on a false accusation by Abspoel, Gustaaf, who entirely without evidence swore under oath to the tribunal of East Flanders that I raped and strangled his underage daughter Rosalie,

I consider it my duty to inform Your Majesty of the fact that I, *grand invalide* and decorated as stated above, am slowly but surely being poisoned in this asylum.

For nine years I have silently and patiently suffered to be taunted and provoked, without a shred of justification, in the most under-handed manner.

A veteran of 1914–18 can tolerate much, and I endured worse ordeals on the Yser. That November night at Ramskapelle, for instance, I will never forget: my leg shattered, I lay in the mud and the dark, wailing like a beast, while enough shrapnel to drive a man mad whistled over my head, and the next morning when the medics, still terrified out of their wits, carried me into the operating room and the doctor said, "You'll just have to clench your teeth, Jerome Corthals, because the truck with morphine and other medicine was shot to smithereens last night two kilometers from here," I suffered more in a few hours than in the past nine years.

That in my first year here, when I was in such a state because of the false allegation of Abspoel, Gustaaf, they strapped me and my one good leg to the bed and more than once forgot to bring me food, even though I've always had a hearty appetite—so be it.

That they did not grant me leave to attend the funeral of my eldest brother Kamiel, who died of throat cancer, because the doctors said the grief could give me a breakdown at that open grave; I, veteran of '14–'18 who stepped over hundreds of corpses without batting an eye and singlehandedly took out three badly-wounded Germans with my bayonet, why would I have had a breakdown at the sight of a neatly nailed-shut coffin, even though my beloved brother was lying in it? Don't make me laugh! Again: so be it.

That they put me in a straitjacket and let three men beat me after, my nerves completely shot, I had grabbed the warder Jean-Marie Delamar by the throat and kept on squeezing until he had, like Rosalie, nearly expired, which would have been his just deserts. Fine. Water under the bridge. I am not one to dwell on bagatelles.

But now that they are slowly, slyly murdering me, the time has come for me to speak out. The comrade who sits here writing this in my stead, because I left school at the age of nine and as a veteran of the front I can hold a rifle far better than a pen, says I should direct my complaint to the Investigating Magistrate or the Crown Solicitor in Ghent, but I know better. Over the years I have written and written, enough to drive one mad. Lawyers, investigating magistrates, crown solicitors, ministers, chairmen of patriotic organizations. Do you think, Sire, that I have received a single answer? Not a one. I seriously doubt whether my letters were even read with appropriate attention.

Therefore I have decided to resort to heavy artillery and appeal directly to Your Majesty, the highest Authority, and the grandson of the dear departed Soldier-King Albert, under whose command I allowed that leg of mine to be shot off.

It's like this, Sire. For three weeks now I have been given drops. For my nerves, says the doctor, but I have had a nervous condition ever since childhood. Nine years in the asylum have shattered my nerves, and now all of a sudden they come up with these drops. And to what effect? They sap my energy, each day more than the last. At times the room spins, and my heart ticks like a clock after walking just twenty meters. I used to be able to walk twenty kilometers on that one leg and then hold my breath for half a minute, effortlessly.

At first they brought the drops in a glass of water. I laughed out loud at them and hurled the glass through the window. In the days thereafter they snuck the drops into the soup, into the mashed potatoes, into the minced beef, and maybe even into the pudding, which they know I love.

I refused to eat until, after two days, I went cross-eyed from hunger. I have already mentioned having a hearty appetite, Sire. "If you won't eat, we'll jab the drops into your backside," they said. "And how many men will you bring to do it?" I asked. "Ten, if need be," was their answer. I ask you man to man, Sire, is this not craven? Ten men against one crippled veteran.

I started eating again anyway, grudgingly. And now here I sit: lethargic, with buttermilk in my eyes, sawdust in my one leg, and a shooting gallery in my heart. Another three weeks of this and I'm a gone goose.

Now, I ask you, Sire, can you turn a blind eye to these torments of a war veteran who sacrificed a leg for the fatherland?

Of course, this is all the fault of the warder Jean-Marie Delamar, who cannot stand the sight of me since I leapt at his throat in legitimate self-defense, and who has encouraged the doctor to quietly do away with me. He stands there leering whenever I eat my soup or my pudding, and when I give him a dirty look he bursts out laughing. If I did not feel so tame, I would hold his face in the soup until he choked in it.

I wished to inform you of this, Sire, in the hope that you and your ministers would call for an investigation into this matter. For if the King does not stand up the just treatment and the lives of his war veterans, then I ask you: why then did we win the War of '14-'18?

With the utmost respectful and sincerest regards, I undersign, your humble servant,

Jerome Corthals.

LESSON IN PHILOSOPHY

Casimir and I stood under the elder tree in the garden talking about happiness.

Casimir held the all-time record for occupancy in the asylum: thirty-two years. He was of Bulgarian extraction, and his crime was so heinous that it was known to only a few, and no one dared utter it out loud.

With his imposing figure, manicured moustache and steely blue eyes, he had the look of a well-preserved officer in retirement. He had impeccable manners and a pride that gave him an unapproachable air. Few were privy to his crime, and few enjoyed his trust. Alongside his soldierly bearing and his pent-up pride, Casimir possessed an extraordinary memory. He had read and re-read every book in the library, and had assembled an encyclopedic scrapbook of magazine articles on an endless variety of topics. He knew the

Petite Larousse more or less by heart. For aficionados of crosswords and brainteasers who happened to be in his good graces, he was an inexhaustible font of knowledge. The distance between Earth and Venus, the tallest peak of the Atlas Mountains, the secular evolution of the arctic lupine, the chemical makeup of seawater—Casimir knew it all.

And if he was in a meditative mood, he would sometimes give me a lesson in philosophy. Like on that Sunday afternoon in the garden.

"Happiness," he opined, "does not exist. It is an abstract invention of man, an attempt to assign a name to the sublimation of his aspirations. In his limitations, man strives, with plaintive nostalgia for a lost paradise that never existed, for the impossibility of perfection and the absolute. He gives human names and forms to his superhuman yearnings: God, freedom, innocence, eternity, love, spirituality, space. Such yearnings are absurd, and in that absurdity, mankind persists in the painful and fruitless enterprise of tearing himself away from his inevitable shortcomings. Only when man, in cold, logical reflection, recognizes his natural limitations and accepts that he will never achieve absolute perfection, and by corollary that God, freedom, innocence, eternity, et cetera do not exist, will life beyond good and evil become bearable. It is the art of compromise."

This thesis was crystal clear and, of course, as old as the hills. He had probably read it somewhere in Kant, Hegel, Schopenhauer, or perhaps Sartre. Or in any given novel by Zola.

"And yet," I said, "all people, even those in the most desperate circumstances, continue to strive for happiness. So the impossible must have something compelling about it."

"Clearly," he replied. "Of course man strives to satisfy his longings, and the ultimate goal of those longings is what we call happiness."

That, too, he had read somewhere. In Sigmund Freud, the go-to philosopher of all insane intellectuals.

It was surprising to hear such a lucid expression of acceptance and relativism from someone who, like Icarus, had recklessly and senselessly defied the limitations of the human condition, and had since lain groaning on his bloodied wings for thirty-two years. Was this acceptance the ripe fruit of his incarceration? Or was he simply parroting a well-worn lesson?

"If happiness does not exist, then logically neither does unhappiness," I said. "There is an Indian mystic making the rounds at the moment. He claims a person can alleviate all his shortcomings and afflictions through meditation and reflection. He also preaches the attainment of inner balance through compromise. After all these years, have you succeeded in honing the art of compromise to the point where you can live in captivity without being unhappy?"

It was a shameless, almost insolent question, which cut to the core of his being and would likely wound his pride.

He shrugged. "Freedom is a matter of independence. I am no more dependent than anyone else here. I am bound to the guards, and the guards are bound to me. My chains are only symbolic; the guards, however, are chained to their wives, their children, their job, their television, their social norms. They bring me food, give me medicine, and must not let me out of their sight for even a minute. For every step I take, a guard must likewise take a step. I choose where we go. True, it's a delineated, restricted area, but he must follow me. So, in fact, I myself am more free than those guards."

Something about his argument was not quite right, but I saw no point in bursting his bubble, so I kept quiet.

Above our heads, the elder tree spread its fragrance, and a blackbird chirped, announcing that rain was on the way.

"What is the name of that Indian mystic?" he asked after a while.

"Maharishi Mahesh Yogi," I said.

Casimir wrote the name meticulously in a small notebook. With a look of smug satisfaction, he wet his mustache with the tip of his tongue.

"Another one of those charlatans I'll have to rub out," he said.

"Charlatans?" I asked innocently.

"Unscrupulous con men who steal my ideas and claim all the glory for themselves. When I get out of here, I will liquidate them all, one by one."

He glanced furtively to both sides and then showed me his notebook, which contained a hit list of some twenty illustrious names. Sure enough, Sartre was one of them.

THE RULES OF THE GAME

"What is your preferred opening? Sicilian or East-Indian?" he asked.

I studied the chessmen, neatly lined up in battle formation on the board.

"Oh," I said, "I open as the mood strikes me. I am not a professional player."

"It's important that I know your opening move," he insisted. "You must play by the rules of the game."

I looked at him more closely. Half an hour earlier he had been led into the dayroom: a dark-haired young man with somewhat wooden movements, but at first glance, likeable enough. For a while he had stood silently eyeing the assorted company, his hands behind his back. Then he sat down at a table and began to arrange the pieces slowly and meticulously on the board.

When I smiled a brief greeting at him as I passed, he gestured for me to join him for a game.

Why not, I thought. After so long, I was pleased at the prospect of a decent game of chess. But once he insisted on me divulging my battle plan, I regretted the whole undertaking. I am not one to show my hand, and am averse to all forms of methodology. I never play according to a strategy. And so his flat-out command of "You must play by the rules of the game" considerably diminished his likeability, despite his friendly face, warm voice, and genteel manners.

"All right," I said, "if you insist. This time I think I shall employ the Portuguese opening."

This was a wild guess. I had no idea if there was such a thing as a Portuguese opening, and if there was, I had no inkling as to what it entailed. Truly, I never should have sat down in the first place.

After some consideration, I slid a random pawn forward, hoping not to have made an irredeemable gaffe.

He smiled courteously and slid one of his pawns in a similar fashion. So far, so good.

So far so good indeed—for after three turns it was painfully obvious that he had absolutely no clue what he was doing.

Clearly, that "Sicilian or East-Indian opening" bluff of his was meant to intimidate me, and from a tactical standpoint I have to give him credit.

I intentionally dallied somewhat with my breakthrough, and in the sixth move took his bishop, placing his king directly in check.

To my amazement, and with complete disregard for the rules, he took one of my knights and proceeded to announce "Check," even though there was no check in sight.

"Forgive me," I said, "but that is against the rules of the game. You must escape check, and besides, you have no right to just take my knight like that."

He turned pale, and I had the impression that his pupils contracted. Still, he managed to maintain his composure.

"I beg your pardon," he said. "I was momentarily distracted."

Against all conventions, he started clumsily moving pieces around willy-nilly, and I noticed that he took the opportunity to quietly shift two of his pawns a square forward.

When he illegally captured my rook in his next turn, I concluded there was no point whatsoever in continuing the game.

I dramatically laid my king on its side, shook his hand, and said, "I concede. You are the better player."

He was visibly elated and weighed my king in his hand like a precious trophy.

As I made to leave, he caught me by the arm.

"You're forgetting to pay up," he said in utmost earnestness.

"Pay up?" I asked, with genuine surprise.

"You lost, so you owe me a pack of cigarettes," he explained. It was spoken with the same emphasis as his exhortation at the beginning of the match: "You must play by the rules of the game."

He was now very pale, and his nostrils quivered. But I was probably no better off than he.

"You are deluded," I said coolly. "You'll have to ask Santa Claus for that pack of cigarettes."

At this I turned my back, put my hands in my pockets, and headed off to the latrine to piss away my pique.

Luckily, Semmelinck let out a scream. I turned around, and with but an instant to spare, I ducked away from the chessboard that came hurtling at me.

The board clattered across the green floor tiles, and I only just managed to catch the dark-haired young man in my arms, his face contorted into a wild grimace, as he was seized by an epileptic fit.

WHITE WAS THE TOMCAT

The way he stood straddle-legged in the stairwell doorway, massive and menacing, with bulging eyeballs and bloodied hands, made me think of the blind, raging Oedipus.

A cold, damp silence descended over the dayroom, and everyone held their breath as they watched the grimacing Jules Leroy hold up the limp corpse of a cat by its tail, like a gruesome trophy. It was the white tomcat Pushkin, much loved by all the inmates. His head was smashed to a pulp. The brain oozed, white and slimy, out of the skull; his black snout had been ripped open above the incisors, frozen in a final, gruesome scream; one congealed eye dangled out of its socket, like a marble hanging from a blue tendon; and the dark, sticky blood trickled slowly onto the tile floor before Jules's feet. Amid all this nauseating carnage, the cat's fur had, somehow, remained spotlessly white.

Jules Leroy had bashed the cat's head against the wall because it had made off with his slice of roast beef. It was a Sunday, and standard Sunday lunch fare was a thin slice of roast beef with potatoes. Jules took his roast beef very seriously indeed. He would meticulously wrap it in newspaper and stow it under his shirt before wolfing down the potatoes with a mound of vegetables. Later that afternoon, he would savor the slice of roast beef with earnest devotion, as though it were a rare delicacy. He would sprinkle it with salt, and sometimes, in exchange for an apple or half a bar of chocolate, Kerhofs would lend him his much-coveted bottle of Worcestershire sauce. That Sunday afternoon, however, Pushkin, in a fit of reckless audacity, had stolen the slice of roast beef from the tin mess kit under Jules's bed.

I was more surprised than upset that Jules had killed the cat. He loved the animal with a childlike fondness, often strutting about with Pushkin atop his broad shoulders. On Fridays he would gather up fish scraps for him in a special container, and had once even knocked Grégoire senseless for having kicked Pushkin out of spite. Grégoire could count himself lucky that it wasn't *his* head Jules had smashed against the wall. I knew he was always prepared to stick up for Pushkin, but I had no idea that he was so defensive about his roast beef.

Jules stood for perhaps a full minute or more in the doorway, motionless and deathly silent, holding the bleeding, mauled carcass.

Then the guard made a cautious and calculated approach, his head cocked slightly to one side.

"Throw that animal out back behind the firewood," his voice dispassionate yet resolute.

Jules Leroy's bulging eyes turned to meet the guard's serious and slightly pained gaze. Jules's expression was more one of surprise than of guilt, but also with a dark glow of smoldering fury. He took a step back, and the cadaver dangled in his outstretched hand, spattering a splotch of blood onto his shoe.

"Throw the cat out back," the guard repeated. His voice was still firm, but he had gone pale.

Jules advanced two steps, grimacing defiantly. Rather than comply, he tightened his grip on the cat's tail.

The muttering in the dayroom resumed, and Sneyers screeched, "Bastard!" This was most unwise.

Jules became engulfed by a new surge of fury, and in his rage he started swinging the cadaver in a circle above his head; globs of brain and blood spattered over the tables and against the whitewashed walls. Even the guard recoiled in shock. He had no choice but to call for reinforcements.

Five minutes later, a quartet of guards stormed the dayroom. They had taken off their starched white jackets. One held a formless, padded coat under his arm, while another nervously cleaved his way through the onlookers with a rubber truncheon. The scene resembled a prehistoric cave drawing in Lascaux: Jules swinging Pushkin's mangled carcass and the guard wielding his truncheon. Jules didn't stand a chance against the four of them. He resisted, hollering, kicking, and cursing, but once they eventually secured the straitjacket, he stood there timidly like a shivering, snorting bull confined to a narrow pen. His left eye was purple, his nose swollen, and under the straps his chest heaved like a bellows. One of the guards carefully dabbed his own bleeding lower lip with a checked handkerchief, held gingerly between two fingers.

As they led Jules off, stumbling and defenseless, Sneyers repeated, "Bastard!" But

Jules did not turn his head. A rough gurgle emerged from his throat, and his eyes had the watery gloss occasionally seen in pregnant cows.

In a corner, under the central heating, the dead tomcat lay stretched out, his four pudgy paws tucked under his spotlessly white fur.

MARGARITAS ANTE PORCOS

The first thing I noticed were his arms. I was reading Dos Passos' *State of the Nation* and had stuffed cotton wads in my ears in an attempt to block out the brutal cacophony of the dayroom. I felt a presence beside me but did not look up. Not that I was so enthralled by Dos Passos, but with a bit of practice one cultivates the art of reading with indifference, simply to cancel out the surroundings. He was leaning with both hands on the tabletop, next to the dented coffeepot, and out of the corner of my eye I could read the mottos tattooed in purple-blue letters on his tanned forearms. On the inside of his left arm was a girl's name, Sylvia. In a flourish as touching as it was childish, the *i* was dotted with a minuscule flower. Sylvia with a flower is a darn sight different from Sylvia with a dot. His right arm bore the cryptic inscription "Margaritas ante porcos." The letter *p* had been inked a little too high, so it looked more like "Margaritas ante forcos," which of course made no sense at all.

Precisely which pearls were meant for which swine was, as yet, unclear. Sayings like these can mean anything—or, perhaps, nothing at all. Some hypochondriacs, in their obsessive need to provoke, etch the most absurd nonsense into their forbearing skin. In the Saint-Léonard prison in Liège, my cellmate was an Algerian who had had "COME GET FUCKED" tattooed in French onto his chest. He slept like an innocent babe, with a bare torso and clenched fists, and around his neck he wore a medallion portraying some saint or another, although I don't know if Islam even has saints.

I slowly and deliberately turned a page, pretending to be engrossed in my reading. Sayings bore me in general, and wandering ones are even worse.

"I'm told you've been rotting away here for five years for substance abuse," said the voice above the arms. A languid, bleary voice with a swooning timbre, which for some reason brought to mind the heady scent of carnations.

This time, surprised and annoyed, I did look up from my book. In the asylum it was simply "not done" to bluntly call a person's crime by its name, except during heated arguments. Nearly everyone knew their fellow inmates' offense down to the last detail, but in everyday social contact, the decent thing was to hold one's tongue. Even if the person in question brought it up themselves, it was usually met with suspicious reservation. The delicate silence on matters of guilt and penance was a sort of gentlemen's agreement governing courteous, if not armored, discretion, probably resulting more from an intuitive sense of repressed shame than any actual grasp of one's guilt. A person with warts does not feel guilty for having them, but neither does he go out of his way to advertise it. The young man with the tattooed arms, who unceremoniously spat out my substance abuse like a gob of phlegm, knowingly violated an unwritten but strictly observed rule.

House custom dictated that I should sock him on the jaw, no questions asked, so as to teach him once and for all not to ask impertinent questions. But I have never hit anyone in my life. Except my four-year-old, when he broke my Parker pen. Mohammed may have been right in saying that every adult deserved to be beaten three times a day, but I think I'll pass, because I am well aware that virtually anyone is more powerful, strapping and agile than I. So I serenely claim to be a pacificist, which is nothing more than a cheap excuse to obfuscate the pathetic fact that I am too much of a weakling to back up an argument with a swift upper cut. I do not believe in violence, but alas, history shows there is nothing quite as effective.

"Mind your own business," I snapped.

He was a newbie in the dayroom. Most likely a recent arrival, judging from his trousers. They were too short. I always noticed that for their first few days, a newcomer's trousers were the wrong length. After a while, pant legs and limbs would, through some wondrous process of assimilation, grow or shrink until they eventually met.

The lad was twenty-three years old, twenty-four at most. I have never been much good at guessing people's ages, because I focus more on the eyes than on the rest of the body, and everyone knows that eyes often look much younger than the rest. When our gazes met, I was at once reminded of a line of poetry by Bertus Aafjes: "Eyes, black as wild cherries." Ever since I started spending my many free hours rereading poetry, spurred on by a nostalgia for my more carefree days, verses like this regularly popped into my mind. Often, they left a lasting mark on a first impression.

Those dark and lively eyes were set in a pale, narrow face. Marcel-Marceau eyes affixed to a powdered white mask, atop the vulgar yet fragile mouth of Elvis Presley. A strange mix of brittle, slightly surprised insouciance and goading arrogance. For some reason, I found his to be a friendly face. Even if I could have mustered up the courage and the energy, I couldn't have punched him. It was probably those eyes. And that languid voice.

"Maybe I can help you," he said hesitantly. I looked at him with astonishment and then let out an uneasy laugh. A laugh that hurt somewhere in my chest.

Over the previous five years, half a dozen self-satisfied psychiatrists had tried to help me—presuming that was even their aim, because I am a firm skeptic when it comes to psychiatric charity. When it comes to plumbing the depths of the human psyche, I have more faith in poets than in physicians. Not that poets know the first thing about it either, of course, but at least they occasionally express their journey through the essence of things in mellifluous and moving language.

For five years the psychiatrists had pondered, investigated, and debated the mysterious origins and motives for my irrational escape into a noxious haze. Escape from whom? Escape from what? Escape from where? Escape *to* where? They did not find any answers, the psychiatrists, all they found was more questions.

Despite their encephalograms, their insulin, and their Minnesota tests, they were still unable to get to the bottom of my troubles. Likewise, no amount of nialamide, promazine, haloperidol, orphenadrine, largactil, nozinan, dixyrazine, meprobamate, or the rest of the other goddamn junk in their pharmaceutical stockpile had succeeded in soothing that old, indescribable, and essentially straightforward pain.

And then along comes this perfect stranger, a half-washed youth in ill-fitting trousers and with infantile hieroglyphics on his arms, asking in all seriousness if he might help. It was not a joke. He *meant* it. I could tell from those dark, gleaming eyes of a youthful saint that he meant it.

Was he a missionary, an idealist, a mythomaniac? Had he been dropped on his head as a baby and now fancied himself a messenger of love? He did not look dangerous, but I had long learned to be wary of peddlers of good advice.

"Who says I want to be helped?" I demanded. I was still determined not to lower the drawbridge.

He blinked, and this too endeared him to me. "May I sit down?" he asked.

This fellow was full of surprises. It was the first time anyone here had heeded the long-forgotten rules of courtesy and asked my permission to sit down. People just sat, stood, lay, and loitered wherever and whenever they pleased, without considering whether someone else might find it inconvenient. There was always a shortage of space in the dayroom. When you went to the latrine, your seat was usually taken by the time you got back. Fistfights over a chair were not unheard of. Only last week, Sander Mielans had attacked Roupcinsky and hurled his shoe through a window because there was nowhere for him to sit down and write his mother a letter.

As it happened, the chair opposite me was free. I nodded, smiled, and made an inviting gesture. Besides, it was his right to sit down; Dos Passos' outdated social-economic musings were boring me, and I was intrigued by the evangelistic exclamation of "Margaritas ante porcos."

As he sat down, I noticed that he was missing the top joint of his left index finger.

Deformities always make me uncomfortable. They give me the feeling that, even before the first skirmish, my primary weapons are blunted. And nowhere was a man more vulnerable without proper weaponry than here in this hermitically sealed arena, where senseless danger constantly lurked behind every corner.

Perhaps he noticed my glance, for he cupped his right hand over the amputated left fingertip. I was thankful for the gesture.

Jean-Claude and De Negus, who were seated at our table for a round of backgammon on a miniature homemade board, looked up from their game.

"You owe me a ciggie if I roll a double six," Jean-Claude said. He kissed the dice, holding them lovingly between his thumb and index finger, and cast them with the gracious toss of a seed-sower. A three and a four.

"*Demain*," said De Negus. "In your dreams." He threw a pair of fours and slapped the table triumphantly, rattling the lid of the coffeepot.

I lit up a Johnson and hesitated as I held the pack. I was always short of cigarettes, and at times was reduced to mooching them off the others. But I offered him one anyway. Maybe he hadn't had a smoke in days. Above the flame of the match, he blinked again. I wondered if it was a tic.

"What's your name?" I asked.

He knew my name and my warts. Someone had evidently filled him in, and while I could demand accountability, I had no appetite for the senseless palaver it would require. Sooner or later, I would find out who had blabbed. For all it mattered. I could already guess that it was that incorrigible fishwife Heck.

"Everyone calls me Bennie," he said. "My name is Benedict Schmitt, with a double t, German spelling. But I prefer Bennie."

"Benedict is the glorious appellation of popes and saints," I said. "Your parents must have been pious folk."

He shrugged his narrow shoulders. "My grandfather was named Benedict, and he was hardly a saint. He died during a fit of barrel fever."

I couldn't pass up the temptation to test him. "I don't see why a saint can't die in a fit of delirium tremens," I said. "Striving for sainthood is a sort of delirium in itself. And drinking can be a way to expand one's mind. Or, conversely, a reaction to the insight that striving for sainthood and expanding one's mind, or whatever you want to call that disease, is nothing but a utopian fantasy. Drink, in that case, can be cathartic."

"Like dope?"

He was no fool, this Bennie. I had to be doubly on my guard. And why was I reminded of carnations for a second time, when he brought up that damn dope again?

"Listen, Bennie," I said. I caught myself feeling a mellifluous pleasure in uttering his name. "I have nothing against you sitting down with me if there's a seat free. I'll offer you the occasional cigarette and you can drink my coffee, because I'm too generous for my own good. Cigarettes and coffee are the only decent things you'll get in this joint, and they're usually scarce. We'll talk about football, about pretty girls, about the war in Vietnam, about anything you want. On one condition. That you keep your trap shut when it comes to that so-called substance abuse. Take it or leave it."

"I was only trying to help," he said, a bit put out. "I used to work in an Indonesian restaurant in Amsterdam. I knew a half-blood there who kicked the habit through yoga and lemon juice. Half an hour of yoga every morning, and a full glass of lemon juice after every meal."

Yoga and lemon juice were the last thing I expected. All things considered, the remedy was no less plausible than all the psychotherapy, niamid and haloperidol the psychiatrists doled out, but I was struck by its naïve simplicity.

He gave me an innocent look. "Why the poker face?"

I shrugged and replied, "Because your story is either too stupid or too tragic to smile about. What was your Indonesian addicted to? Aspirin?"

"He wasn't Indonesian, he was a half-blood," Bennie said, in a way that told me the distinction was of some significance to him. "He took Benzedrine for more than a year, and I swear he managed to shake the stuff with yoga and lemon juice. It sounds crazy, I admit, but it's the God-honest truth."

I blew cigarette smoke at his face, but he didn't flinch. So that blinking of his was not a tic. "The truth is, Simple Simon: your half-blood was having you on. I have no experience with Benzedrine; yoga, aside from the fact that it is undoubtedly a tiring occupation, is a closed book to me; and a glass of lemon juice sounds like a disgusting concoction. I consider this chapter closed. If you're not prepared to avoid the subject from now on, then I suggest you beat it."

"All right," he said. "If that's what you want, I'll go sit somewhere else."

I was amused by his spontaneous pique. I like that kind of pride. I impulsively lay a hand on his arm, the Sylvia arm. "There are plenty of other interesting things we could talk about," I said, to smooth things over. "Like the pearls before the swine. What pearls are you throwing to which swine?"

With his left hand, the hand with the finger stump, he rubbed his right arm, the one emblazoned with the verse from St. Matthew. I got the impression that he was a little embarrassed by it.

"It's nothing," he said. "I worked on a tanker for fourteen months. All the guys got tattoos. Sailors see it as a sort of badge of their profession. Mine's a souvenir of Port Said. For five bucks, you can have any text you want. A naked woman costs three times that."

So Bennie Schmitt had worked in an Indonesian restaurant in Amsterdam, had sailed on a tanker, and now he was in an asylum. He couldn't have been older than twenty-two and he already had a history.

"So why 'Margaritas ante porcos'?" I pressed. "Why not, for example, 'Vergissmeinnicht' or 'Born to Raise Hell' or 'Mort aux Vaches'? As far as I know, these sayings are more common to the genre."

A melancholy smile formed around his healthy white teeth. "Why not 'Margaritas ante porcos'? It was just a whim. You don't have to know Latin or worship St. Matthew to appreciate a poetic, melodious turn of phrase. The old Turk in Port Said apparently thought it was a perfectly normal thing to tattoo on your arm. Probably thought it was some lovey-dovey Spanish or Italian saying. If you just listen to the sound without bothering with the meaning, it could be a line from an old-time ballad."

He was right, but I only half-believed him. I didn't buy that tale of an adventurous youth spending the price of a bottle of whisky or a harborside whore on an unrhymed poetic fancy. It was almost too good to be true, and his explanation sounded too contrived to be plausible. I was almost certain that behind the cryptic motto lay a deeper significance he was not yet ready to divulge. Maybe that tattoo was the bandage on his warts. Maybe he had never set foot in Port Said. After all, he had just as much right to cover up his sores as I did.

"You are an odd bird," I said, "but I think we'll get along. I have a weakness for odd romantics who find poetry in the most unlikely places, and then have it scorched into their skin like a costly and cherished possession.

I'll warn you, though: you're unlikely to find much poetry in this hole."

"Va chier à la gare!"[1] Jean-Claude shouted in his raspy voice. He had leapt up and angrily threw the dice at the fat, grinning face of De Negus. De Negus was an incorrigible cheater; it was an irresistible urge even though in the main he was a decent fellow. He had even come up with an ingenious way to cheat at solitaire without even noticing it himself. Because of this unfortunate quirk, almost no one would play games with him. Except Jean-Claude, who also cheated.

It looked as though it would come to blows, but Jean-Claude, who had just spent two weeks in solitary confinement, straps and all, quickly thought better of it and decided it would suffice to repeat "Va chier à la gare!" at the top of his lungs. It was his favorite catchphrase.

Bennie had slid his chair to the far corner of the table, just to be on the safe side. He did his best to adopt a nonchalant pose, but I noticed his breathing was faster than before.

I shrugged in resignation. "Excuse the *porcos*," I said.

He responded to my gesture with a shallow smile and blew his nose into one of those

---

1 "Take a flying fuck!"

absurd blue plaid handkerchiefs that always made me think of some Polish or Russian girl. Surely another tic, that nose-blowing.

Just then, Cyril came sauntering in from the garden and demanded his chair back, as though he were its legitimate owner.

I lost track of Bennie as the evening wore on. Bored and tired, I read another chapter in *State of the Nation*, played a round of rami bridge and won a can of pilchards. I never eat pilchards.

Later, on our way to the dormitory, the guard took me aside. "Birds of a feather," he said.

"Meaning?" I asked, trying my best to keep distance.

"Didn't the newbie tell you he's one of your lot? Narcotics. Bad habit he picked up on board a ship."

"And what was his bad habit, then?" I snarled.

"Amphetamines," said the guard. "You might want to take him under your wing. His first few days and weeks won't be easy."

An extremely vulgar word formed on the tip of my tongue, but I reconsidered and proceeded silently to the dormitory.

He slept diagonally across from me, Bennie Schmitt, directly in my line of sight.

Before he slid under the covers, he waved me good night. Skinny and fragile in his white pajamas, he looked so pure that I struggled to envision any guilt on his part.

When I got up half an hour later to smoke a cigarette in the latrine, he lay motionless in bed, staring at the ceiling. I avoided making eye contact, but I knew we would forever be bound to one another, like lepers in the Middle Ages. It made me feel less alone.

The night watchman trod silently on his rubber-soled shoes through the dormitory, his hands behind his back, amid the usual bothersome yet comforting sounds that live between sleep and waking. In the corner, the old asthmatic Gyselinck snored loudly, like every night; across the room, Siedlecki mumbled unintelligible monosyllables, like every night; two beds further down, Armand was busy masturbating, just like every night. Like every night.

Back in bed, I pulled the covers over my head and tried to imagine what Sylvia looked like. She was tall and slender, and probably pretty, too. Perhaps she was blonde. I wondered if she wore blue jeans.

I woke up the next morning to a strangely tense atmosphere in the dormitory. I felt it even before I opened my eyes. Two guards and a pale medic stood on either side of Bennie's bed. They spoke in hushed voices and formed a tight circle, so that I could only see their backs. Ominous backs. The medic slid his cap back a bit and then pulled the sheet over Bennie's head. In his hand was an empty box of dextroamphetamine.

I do not remember how I washed or dressed. I must have mechanically made my way downstairs, past the bed with the all-too-white sheet.

The pain came later when I was standing in line for the steaming pot of hot water, the dented coffeepot in my hand, while the cheery "Big Fat Alice" theme song blared its exuberant trumpets and roaring trombones, as it did every morning, through the loudspeakers.

I will never know if the yoga and the lemon juice were made up. I will never know what Sylvia looked like. And I will never know what pearls he wasted on which swine.

ARTISTE PEINTRE

There was a time when Gerard Brasseur painted landscapes, still lifes, and portraits with the skill of a craftsman and the acumen of a capitalist. Brasseur the citizen prospered, but Brasseur the artist came to hate the bourgeois hackwork on which he willfully squandered his talent.

With childlike pride, and yet a hint of self-consciousness, he showed me the posters and invitations announcing his exhibitions: "Gerard Brasseur, artiste peintre, expose son oeuvre dans les salons Artes." He pressed black-and-white photographs of his work into my hand, which by definition were devoid of color. But I doubt that these hopelessly conventional paintings of farmsteads, autumn flowers, and fishermen's tronies had had much color to begin with. Most likely plenty of brown, red, and green; without nuance, without flair. Gerard Brasseur, *artiste peintre raté*, failed painter.

"Nice," I said with friendly approval, for I did not wish to offend him.

But he knew better, and shook his head. His self-consciousness won out over his pride. He contemptuously threw the photos on the floor, as proof that they were junk.

And they *were* junk. Still, he had fared well in a material sense, selling his mechanically executed canvases (often copied from postcards) to specialized shops catering to the well-to-do. He could have continued in this vein, accumulating a tidy nest egg and assuaging his artistic conscience with the self-deception that Utrillo, too, had made a living copying postcards.

For seven years, Gerard Brasseur soldiered on. Then one day he took a bread knife and slashed all his canvases to ribbons, abandoned his sobbing wife, and headed off to the harborside brothels with the studio cash box under his arm.

In less than a week he burned through more than a hundred thousand francs. For another week he lurched from one seedy tavern to the next, and was ultimately admitted, shivering from head to toe and flat broke, to the psychiatric unit of the local hospital with a severe case of delirium tremens.

During his first days in the hospital he drank copious amounts of water, received injections, and gradually regained his appetite and his strength, but stubbornly refused to see his wife or any other members of his family.

Six weeks later he was discharged from the hospital. He withdrew his last sixty thousand francs from the bank, barricaded himself in a rented room in the shadow of the cathedral, and started painting again.

Vertical and horizontal lines, circles, ovals, static and pure geometric figures in bold colors. A modest but revealing excursion into the clear-cut world of Mondrian.

He peddled his new works among the dealers. They shrugged their shoulders.

For two weeks he sat in his rented room brooding and boozing among all that geometry. Then came the sudden eruption of what he believed to be his true talent. He threw himself into the violence of shapeless yet very tangible abstraction. No lines, no contours. Only colors. Brushes and palettes were tossed aside in scorn. He turned unwittingly to "action painting," squeezing brilliant colors directly from the tubes onto the canvas and wrestling them into submission on the flat, patient surface. After an exhausting effort he stood, panting, before the manifestation of a nameless emotion. The heat of this expression elicited in him a sort of sexual arousal; occasionally he got an erection while painting, but he paid it no heed. The colors were all that mattered.

Again, off he went to the art dealers. They eyed him with suspicion that verged on alarm. Unsellable stuff.

Shortly thereafter, one Sunday afternoon, Gerard Brasseur raped a twelve-year-old girl along the deserted waterfront. In a panic, he strangled the child and threw her body into the Meuse. One hour later, bawling and cursing, he turned himself in to the police.

In the asylum they gave him a room to himself, because the doctors believed that painting would relieve his mental strain. That room became his asylum-within-an-asylum. Only a select few were admitted to the cell, and if ever he had to report elsewhere, he bolted the door with a mighty padlock.

Each visit I paid Gerard Brasseur was an adventure. He had his lucid moments, when he would talk calmly and intelligently in the dimly-lit and inconceivably messy studio about erstwhile East Asian civilizations, Sumerian pottery, Egyptian bas reliefs, Chinese bronzes, and Indian architecture. I noticed that he seldom brought up Western visual arts and never mentioned the modernists. He did, however, sometimes recite verses of Baudelaire and De Musset by heart. At those times his jaundiced, monkish complexion took on a translucent sheen.

He also had his emotional crises, during which he would smear everything at hand liberally with paint, without any figurative or rational plan whatsoever. The doctors declared that these explosions were more curative than most medications.

One afternoon, when I went around to return a book, I found Gerard Brasseur sitting stock-still in his armchair, seized by a singular, undefined anxiety. He had painted his head in outrageous colors, like some Congolese warrior. The paint clung to his skin in thick, greasy daubs, dripping into his mouth and ears. In each ear he had stuck a paper flower.

When I asked if there was anything I could do for him, he stuck out his tongue, which he had painted in the most odious yellow I have ever seen.

When I noticed the absence of the huge padlock the next day, I knew that Gerard Brasseur had been transferred to the special unit where, according to the asylum's brochure, "patients in need of special care are attended to by committed and qualified personnel."

LIVINUS'S FAREWELL

The doctors had given the eighty-three-year-old Livinus one more week to live, give or take a day.

The asylum officials had sent a telegram to the family to this effect. So on that October afternoon, Livinus's daughter and son-in-law stood at the old man's bedside to discreetly say their goodbyes.

Farewells demand a certain measure of ceremony. The daughter untied the pink ribbon from the cardboard box and, as though handling a precious and fragile artefact, carefully removed a cake. With a self-satisfied smile, she slid the delicacy on its paper doily across the tray table until it was right under her father's nose.

Sunk deep in his hospital bed, old Livinus bent his bald, birdlike head forward ever so slightly and inspected the baked goods with a clouded but critical eye. His right hand trembled like a leaf and his lips quivered above the offering. Then with his emaciated but still-functioning left hand, he shoved the cake away from him. A dab of whipped cream stuck to his finger. He glowered at his daughter with a menacing, almost hateful look. "I want a jenever," he said.

The woman pursed her lips and looked coolly at her husband, who stood, flushed and sheepish, on the other side of the bed. Being confronted with this sudden dilemma made him look even more useless. His Adam's apple bobbed up and down, but he was at a loss.

"Be sensible now and have a piece of cake," said the daughter.

It sounded like a reprimand, almost an order. She struggled to pull her taut face back into a smile and prepared to dig the knife into the cake.

"I want a jenever," Livinus repeated. His right hand, resting on the bedsheet, started shaking more violently than before, and he looked as though he would rather die on the spot than take even a single bite of that cake.

"Cake tastes better with a glass of milk," the son-in-law cautiously volunteered. He said it without conviction, for he knew better. But he was expected to at least make an attempt. He was doing his best.

"I want a jenever," Livinus said for the third time, and so loudly that the entire ward could hear it. Saliva trickled between his rotten teeth, and he was close to losing his temper. "I like jenever more than cake," he added, as though to say, *case closed.*

It was the truth. He liked jenever more than anything else, and this was the cause of all his misery. When he had reached for the ax, years ago, he had also been drinking jenever.

"Liquor's bad for your heart, Pa," said the woman. "And for your kidneys. Doctor's orders."

Her face stiffened, and she shot her husband a warning glance across the bed.

Judging from old Livinus's angry grimace, he profoundly loathed the doctor. He likely also profoundly loathed his heart and kidneys, his daughter and son-in-law, and all the rest of that damnation. He groaned and sunk back into his pillow, and his ire appeared to dissolve into a murmur of misery. "I wish I was dead," he moaned, with the tone of a querulous child.

An embarrassed silence fell around his bed, which befitted the somber evocation of his wish to die.

The son-in-law, with a skittish look in his eye, nervously approached his wife and whispered, "Say I went out and bought him some. There's a liquor store around the corner. They'll have hip flasks of that abominable low-grade stuff. One drink—what harm could it do? He'll be dead in a week anyway."

The old man leered at the conspirators with intense interest. He hoisted himself from his pillow again, revitalized by a sudden surge of hope.

The woman retreated into silent deliberation. After a brief but evidently torturous inner conflict, she said with the tone of a person washing their hands of all guilt, "I'll have nothing to do with it. You'll have to ask the nurse."

She did not want it on her conscience that her father might die a week too soon. She might also have guessed that the nurse was an impenetrable fortress. The son-in-law vacillated for a moment, and then shuffled furtively off on his rubber soles to the glass-enclosed nurses' station, where a spindly, bespectacled matron was busy filling various vials.

The man blushingly made his request. The nurse looked at him as though he had made some bold, depraved proposal, and indignantly shook her head.

The son-in-law shuffled back to the bed like a wounded soldier returning from defeat on the battlefield. “She said no,” he reported. The rest got stuck in his throat. His hands resting on the bedspread were far too large, and just as useless as the rest of his body.

“I thought so,” the woman said, in the same cool tone of voice, but with a ripple of triumph.

Old Livinus fell back onto his pillow and shut his eyes. He lay there motionless, like a wax figure. The only discernible movement was in his lips, which continued to mutter tiny, inaudible words. He was in effect already starting to decompose. He smelled of household soap and humus.

“*One* jenever,” he moaned without opening his eyes. “Just one jenever before I die. And the answer is *no*. Truly, I wish I was dead.”

And he undoubtedly meant it.

Again they were cloaked in an oppressive silence, as if they were indeed standing at his deathbed. There was nothing more to say. The stubborn old man had retreated into death’s chilly waiting room, where words were of no more use.

The daughter lay a hand on her father’s left arm, the working one. “We’ll come back when you’re feeling better,” she said.

The son-in-law looked down at his gleaming shoes. He knew there would be no more “feeling better.”

With deft, dexterous fingers, the woman smoothed the bedspread and cast one last hesitant glance at the cake. Leave it here or take it with them? She shrugged her shoulders and walked with a heavy tread toward the exit, where a ward attendant stood waiting with administrative papers. The son-in-law trailed her silently, like a sleepwalker. He avoided looking at the other beds as he passed, all of them occupied by elderly men.

Once they were out of sight, Livinus drew the cake closer. He looked at it intently, then spat squarely between the two maraschino cherries in the middle of the cake. He then called out loudly for the bedpan.

TRUMPET

Never before had I heard anyone play the trumpet like Honoré. One couldn't actually call it playing. It was groaning and grumbling and wailing and practically cursing through the instrument. Howling, drawn-out, discordant tones, so shrill and mistuned that it cut you to the quick. The lamentations of Orpheus on the loss of his Eurydice could not have sounded more woeful.

The trumpet was Doctor Poulard's idea. While paging through the patient's dossier, he discovered that Honoré had played the trumpet before being admitted to the asylum. Doctor Poulard regarded this as an important element. He subscribed to the opinion held widely by psychiatrists that creative aptitude manifested in one's youth and abandoned for whatever reason should be stimulated, with patience and, if necessary, gentle insistence, for this was a positive way—according to the psychiatrists, at least—of releasing one's tensions. He who once painted, must resume painting, no matter if by now he could not face another tube of paint. Who once partook of music as a pastime but had long come to the conclusion that installing kitchen cabinets was a more lucrative profession, must be nudged back to the spurned Polyhymnia. It is a wonder that Doctor Poulard never encouraged me to write; he was probably unaware that in my youth I had tried my hand at love poems.

After some searching, one of the guards found in his attic a long-disused, copper-colored instrument, something between a piston bugle and a cornet—for the sake of simplicity a "trumpet"—and they persuaded Honoré to release his tensions upon it. During the day he was given a place all to himself in the dining hall, and the doctor eagerly awaited the results of the experiment.

This experiment was of particular interest because Honoré had not uttered a single word since entering the asylum. His vocal and auditory organs were in perfect working order, but for a reason only he knew, if there was any reason at all, he stubbornly refused to engage in any form of dialogue. Perhaps that ornery, impermeable silence was a form of passive resistance. Or maybe nothing much happened behind that forehead anymore that warranted being put into words.

This apathy taken into account, Doctor Poulard saw it as a positive sign that Honoré was prepared to blow the trumpet at all, even though it had nothing to do with music, nor was there any indication, from the onset of this exercise, of the lessening of tensions.

"Keep at it," said Doctor Poulard. "We're on the right track."

For a full week Honoré sat in the refectory torturing that instrument. The low notes were bearable. At times it sounded like a passing steamboat. The strident high-pitched tones, however, caused us to wince and gave the warders migraine. Honoré might be releasing his own tensions, but in the restless dining hall, tensions rose by the day. Even the startled birds indignantly gave the garden a wide berth.

Doctor Poulard found it curious and also rather disappointing that after a week, no civilized sound could be coaxed out of the trumpet.

"Nevertheless," he said, "there it is, in black and white, in his dossier: *son oncle et sa belle-soeur déclarent qu'il joue de la trompette.*"

Then the guard recalled in a flash that in some parts of Wallonia, specifically in the Borinage, whence Honoré hailed, it was sometimes said of an idiot that "he played the trumpet."

Doctor Poulard thought this an excellent joke and the guard, who knew his manners, laughed heartily along with him.

"Absolument fantastique!" exclaimed Doctor Poulard.

He went to the dining hall, where Honoré sat in his corner, blowing diligently, and kindly patted the patient on the shoulder. Then he suddenly grabbed the instrument and hurled it with a mighty sling across the room, in the hope that the shock of it would elicit some sort of response.

That hope went, as before, unfulfilled. Honoré looked in silent astonishment from his empty hands to the guard, and from the guard to Doctor Poulard, with the look of a sick animal unable to say where it hurts.

UNAUTHORIZED ITEMS

After eleven years and nine months, Ernest Bossuyt was finally due to leave the asylum. He had served his time for quite a brazen misstep, and after all the pills and injections, the doctors were now of the opinion that he could once again be considered a useful member of society, and that probation was worth a try.

He stood in the warden's cubicle in a wondrous outfit similar to the shabby clothes worn by displaced persons during those first months after liberation, as they trudged from the German to the American camps. His long overcoat was the color of unripe olives, and his wide, checkered pant legs only just stuck out underneath. The collar of his flannel shirt was secured with a frayed necktie, and on his head he wore a jolly Alpine hat, feather and all. A dozen of our fellow inmates would have fought to the death for that hat.

Bossuyt stared mesmerized at the brown paper bag labelled, in large block letters, PROHIBÉ. The guard shook out the bag's contents and Bossuyt was overcome with unspeakable bliss as the unauthorized items he had been made to surrender upon entering the asylum once again fell within his grasp. It was like unearthing a long-buried treasure.

Bossuyt needed only one covetous glance to assure himself that nothing was missing. He had spent the previous few days taking frequent mental inventory of his personal possessions. There was his wristwatch (a Swiss-made 17-jewel "Donada"); his red-leather billfold with the initials E.B. stamped on the inside; a pocketknife with a mother-of-pearl grip; a Yale padlock with two large keys; his change purse; a cigarette lighter (whose fluid had surely all but evaporated), a stadium pass for F.C. Antwerp's 1955-56 season; a corkscrew with a retractable nail file; and a tram ticket that had been punched four times. The stadium pass and the tram ticket were, of course, worthless after all those years, but according to the regulations, all unauthorized items had to be returned to their rightful owner in their original condition upon his discharge from the asylum.

Bossuyt reached straightaway for the watch. It was his most prized possession. Not only because of its phosphorescent face, intricate workings, and the seventeen jewels. No: at long last, Bossuyt was once again master of his own time. He could arrange and rearrange the hours as he pleased. He could glance at the watch on his left wrist and think to himself: I think I'll go to bed at eleven o'clock today. Or: at eleven o'clock I'll go for a walk, hands in my pockets, and look up at the Milky Way in the night sky, and at a quarter after eleven I'll go drink four beers at Bertha's on the corner. He was not sure whether Bertha's corner bar was still there, but he could walk into any old pub at a quarter past eleven and drink four beers. Or five. Or eight, if he felt like it. From now on, no one could tell him what to do or where to be.

Slowly and meticulously, he wound up the watch and asked the guard for the exact time.

"Ten past nine, on the nose," the guard answered.

Bossuyt set the watch to ten past nine and brought it to his left ear, his delighted eyes fixed on a vague but steady point on the wall behind the guard. The watch ticked rhythmically and earnestly, as though the mechanism had not stopped for even a second those past eleven years and nine months.

"*Ça marche*," Bossuyt said, elated. In French, his satisfaction sounded even more heartfelt.

While Bossuyt clasped the plastic watch-band around his wrist, the guard read out the inventory of unauthorized items from a blue form.

"Sign here," said the guard when he had finished reading the list. It still sounded like a command.

Bossuyt painstakingly signed his name on the dotted line: Ernest A.J. Bossuyt. The letters danced around a bit, but it was otherwise a clearly legible signature.

Smiling, he put the rest of the unauthorized items, which were no longer unauthorized, into the deep pockets of his overcoat. He pressed the Alpine hat firmly onto his head, examined the feather in the cracked mirror next to the wall calendar, and adjusted the knot in his tie. He was ready. After he left, the asylum and all its inhabitants could disintegrate behind him into a smoldering mass of sulfur fumes and ash, for all he cared. He would not look back.

Bossuyt followed the guard down the long corridor to the registry office. His shoes chafed his tender feet, for he had hardly worn anything but slippers for the past eleven years and nine months. It was a pleasant sort of agony: the pinching shoes, like the watch, were part of his impending freedom. He would run the gauntlet to liberty, if need be. In the small registry office, he was given an identification card, the sum of 1,623 francs, and a sealed envelope containing an official referral for employment at a vegetable cannery. Bossuyt read the address and casually stuffed the envelope into his inside pocket. The job did not interest him much. One thousand six hundred and twenty-three francs—now, *that* was a wad of dough.

The guard accompanied him to the gate, turned the key in the lock, and stuck out his hand. "All the best," he said.

Bossuyt shook the hand and tapped the brim of his Alpine hat with one finger. Speechless with anticipation, he veered onto the street in his flapping outfit and picked up his pace, as though he had a train to catch.

The guard watched him through the barred window as he closed the gate. Those hinges really could use oiling, he thought. He calmly rolled a cigarette and saw Bossuyt disappear around the corner. "All the best," he repeated softly.

He lit his cigarette and ambled listlessly back to the dayroom. He knew better than all those doctors that it would only be a matter of days before Bossuyt, broke and most likely blotto, was back in the asylum. And that was still better than letting him suffer miserably out in that messed-up society with its canned vegetables and countless unauthorized items.

TRANSLATOR'S NOTE

Although *De knetterende schedels* was written in Van de Velde's native Dutch, the reader will have noticed that many of the patients and the doctors are French-speaking. Belgium is a bilingual nation and Van de Velde was held in various correctional facilities in francophone Wallonia as well as Dutch-speaking Flanders. That the doctors and wardens converse and keep records in French seems to indicate the dominance of French in those days as the language of scientists, administrators, and bureaucrats.

The Antwerp archives of Flemish literature, the "Letterenhuis," very generously gave me access to Van de Velde's complete dossier, including the manuscript and typoscript of *De knetterende schedels*. The result was a small number of minor additions, deletions, or amendments to the English translation. One major revision was the use of an alternative ending to "Margaritas ante porcos," found in a separate, typed version of this story. It adds an uncharacteristically personal and emotional element to Van de Velde's own drug abuse, and better rounds off the story of Bennie Schmitt.

In addition to Daniëlle Palmans at the Letterenhuis, I am grateful to Van de Velde's biographer Ellen Van Pelt for her input and insight, to my colleague Brent Annable for his astute editorial eye, and to Flanders Literature for their unending support for this project.

—Jonathan Reeder

A PARTIAL LIST OF SNUGGLY BOOKS

MAY ARMAND BLANC *The Last Rendezvous*
G. ALBERT AURIER *Elsewhere and Other Stories*
CHARLES BARBARA *My Lunatic Asylum*
S. HENRY BERTHOUD *Misanthropic Tales*
LÉON BLOY *The Tarantulas' Parlor and Other Unkind Tales*
ÉLÉMIR BOURGES *The Twilight of the Gods*
ADA BUISSON *The Baron's Coffin and Other Disquieting Tales*
CYRIEL BUYSSE *The Aunts*
JAMES CHAMPAGNE *Harlem Smoke*
FÉLICIEN CHAMPSAUR *The Latin Orgy*
BRENDAN CONNELL *Metrophilias*
BRENDAN CONNELL (editor)
The Zinzolin Book of Occult Fiction
RAFAELA CONTRERAS *The Turquoise Ring and Other Stories*
DANIEL CORRICK (editor)
Ghosts and Robbers: An Anthology of German Gothic Fiction
ADOLFO COUVE *When I Think of My Missing Head*
QUENTIN S. CRISP *Aiaigasa*
ALADY DILKE *The Outcast Spirit and Other Stories*
ÉDOUARD DUJARDIN *Hauntings*
BERIT ELLINGSEN *Now We Can See the Moon*
ERCKMANN-CHATRIAN *A Malediction*
ALPHONSE ESQUIROS *The Enchanted Castle*
ENRIQUE GÓMEZ CARRILLO *Sentimental Stories*
DELPHI FABRICE *Flowers of Ether*
DELPHI FABRICE *The Red Spider*
BENJAMIN GASTINEAU *The Reign of Satan*
EDMOND AND JULES DE GONCOURT *Manette Salomon*
REMY DE GOURMONT *From a Faraway Land*
REMY DE GOURMONT *Morose Vignettes*
GUIDO GOZZANO *Alcina and Other Stories*
GUSTAVE GUICHES *The Modesty of Sodom*
EDWARD HERON-ALLEN *The Complete Shorter Fiction*
RHYS HUGHES *Cloud Farming in Wales*
J.-K. HUYSMANS *The Crowds of Lourdes*
J.-K. HUYSMANS *Knapsacks*
COLIN INSOLE *Valerie and Other Stories*
JUSTIN ISIS *Pleasant Tales II*

JULES JANIN *The Dead Donkey and the Guillotined Woman*
GUSTAVE KAHN *The Mad King*
MARIE KRYSINSKA *The Path of Amour*
BERNARD LAZARE *The Mirror of Legends*
BERNARD LAZARE *The Torch-Bearers*
MAURICE LEVEL *The Shadow*
JEAN LORRAIN *Errant Vice*
JEAN LORRAIN *Fards and Poisons*
JEAN LORRAIN *Masks in the Tapestry*
JEAN LORRAIN *Monsieur de Bougrelon and Other Stories*
JEAN LORRAIN *Nightmares of an Ether-Drinker*
JEAN LORRAIN *The Soul-Drinker and Other Decadent Fantasies*
GEORGES DE LYS *An Idyll in Sodom*
GEORGES DE LYS *Penthesilea*
ARTHUR MACHEN *N*
ARTHUR MACHEN *Ornaments in Jade*
CAMILLE MAUCLAIR *The Frail Soul and Other Stories*
CATULLE MENDÈS *Bluebirds*
CATULLE MENDÈS *For Reading in the Bath*
CATULLE MENDÈS *Mephistophela*
ÉPHRAÏM MIKHAËL *Halyartes and Other Poems in Prose*
LUIS DE MIRANDA *Who Killed the Poet?*
OCTAVE MIRBEAU *The Death of Balzac*
CHARLES MORICE *Babels, Balloons and Innocent Eyes*
GABRIEL MOUREY *Monada*
DAMIAN MURPHY *Daughters of Apostasy*
KRISTINE ONG MUSLIM *Butterfly Dream*
OSSIT *Ilse*
CHARLES NODIER *Outlaws and Sorrows*
HERSH DOVID NOMBERG *A Cheerful Soul and Other Stories*
PHILOTHÉE O'NEDDY *The Enchanted Ring*
GEORGES DE PEYREBRUNE *A Decadent Woman*
HÉLÈNE PICARD *Sabbat*
URSULA PFLUG *Down From*
JEAN PRINTEMPS *Whimsical Tales*
JEREMY REED *When a Girl Loves a Girl*
ADOLPHE RETTÉ *Misty Thule*
JEAN RICHEPIN *The Bull-Man and the Grasshopper*
DAVID RIX *A Blast of Hunters*
FREDERICK ROLFE (Baron Corvo) *Amico di Sandro*

JASON ROLFE *An Archive of Human Nonsense*
ARNAUD RYKNER *The Last Train*
MARCEL SCHWOB *The Assassins and Other Stories*
MARCEL SCHWOB *Double Heart*
CHRISTIAN HEINRICH SPIESS *The Dwarf of Westerbourg*
BRIAN STABLEFORD (editor)
Decadence and Symbolism: A Showcase Anthology
BRIAN STABLEFORD (editor) *The Snuggly Satyricon*
BRIAN STABLEFORD (editor) *The Snuggly Satanicon*
BRIAN STABLEFORD *Spirits of the Vasty Deep*
COUNT ERIC STENBOCK *Love, Sleep & Dreams*
COUNT ERIC STENBOCK *Myrtle, Rue & Cypress*
COUNT ERIC STENBOCK *The Shadow of Death*
COUNT ERIC STENBOCK *Studies of Death*
MONTAGUE SUMMERS *The Bride of Christ and Other Fictions*
MONTAGUE SUMMERS *Six Ghost Stories*
ALICE TÉLOT *The Inn of Tears*
GILBERT-AUGUSTIN THIERRY
Reincarnation and Redemption
DOUGLAS THOMPSON *The Fallen West*
TOADHOUSE *Gone Fishing with Samy Rosenstock*
TOADHOUSE *Living and Dying in a Mind Field*
TOADHOUSE *What Makes the Wave Break?*
LÉO TRÉZENIK *The Confession of a Madman*
LÉO TRÉZENIK *Decadent Prose Pieces*
RUGGERO VASARI *Raun*
ILARIE VORONCA *The Confession of a False Soul*
JANE DE LA VAUDÈRE *The Demi-Sexes and The Androgynes*
JANE DE LA VAUDÈRE
The Double Star and Other Occult Fantasies
AUGUSTE VILLIERS DE L'ISLE-ADAM *Isis*
RENÉE VIVIEN AND HÉLÈNE DE ZUYLEN DE NYEVELT
Faustina and Other Stories
RENÉE VIVIEN *Lilith's Legacy*
RENÉE VIVIEN *A Woman Appeared to Me*
ILARIE VORONCA *The Confession of a False Soul*
ILARIE VORONCA *The Key to Reality*
TERESA WILMS MONTT *In the Stillness of Marble*
TERESA WILMS MONTT *Sentimental Doubts*
KAREL VAN DE WOESTIJNE *The Dying Peasant*

Printed in the USA
CPSIA information can be obtained
at www.ICGtesting.com
JSHW080319010224
56122JS00004B/148

9 781645 251132